A MEDICAL CENTER

The Cradle of Medical Education
in the District of Columbia.

The "old Medical College" on the northeastern corner of 10th and E Streets, built by the Medical faculty at its own expense in 1825 and occupied by them until 1834, and again from 1839 to 1844. From 1868 to 1886, the building was occupied by the Medical School of Georgetown University. (From an original drawing by Peter Nelson in the University Collection.)

ELMER LOUIS KAYSER

A MEDICAL
CENTER

The Institutional Development of
Medical Education in
George Washington University

WASHINGTON

GEORGE WASHINGTON UNIVERSITY PRESS

To
MY FATHER
in memoriam

Contents

Illustrations

The Cradle of Medical Education in the District of Columbia.

Frontispiece

These pictures follow page 14

Luther Rice (1783-1836), Founder of Columbian College.

Title Page of President Staughton's Inaugural.

William Staughton, D.D., First President of Columbian College, 1821-1827.

Thomas Sewall, M.D., First President of the Medical Faculty.

James Martin Staughton, M.D.

Joseph Borrows (1807-1889), A.B., 1825, M.D., 1828.

The First Printed Circular of the Medical Department.

Title Page of Dr. Sewall's Address, Marking the Formal Opening of Instruction in the Medical Department.

Student Cards of Thomas Sewall at the University of Pennsylvania.

Cards for the Lectures of Dr. Thomas P. Jones (1773-1848).

These pictures follow page 46

The Dean's Book, Vol. I, p. 1.

The Washington Infirmary.

Destruction of the Infirmary, 1861.

Sisters of Charity.

Thomas Miller, M.D., President of the Faculty.

Harvey Lindsly, M.D., President of the American Medical Association.

These pictures follow page 78

These pictures follow page 110

The North Side of H Street After the Marvin Renovation.

Theobald Smith (1859-1934), M.D.

Walter Reed (1851-1902), M.D.

Frederick Fuller Russell (1870-1960), M.D.

William Fowke Ravenel Phillips, M.D., Dean of the Medical School, 1904-1909.

Emil Alexander deSchweinitz, M.D., Dean of the Medical School, 1897-1904.

Joseph Ford Thompson, M.D., Last President of the Medical Faculty, 1887-1898.

William Cline Borden, M.D., Dean of the Medical School, 1909-1931.

Nurses' Home, 1913-1931.

Designation of University Hospital as General Hospital 75, World War I.

Roland Walton, D.D.S., Dean, 1909-1918.

Henry C. Thompson, D.D.S., President of the Dental Faculty, 1887-1898.

J. Hall Lewis, D.D.S., Dean of the Dental School, 1894-1909.

Mary Winifred Glasscock, R.N.

Lintel Post of the Stairs.

Library, Medical School.

Hall A, Medical School.

Laboratories, Medical School.

These pictures follow page 142

Pennsylvania Avenue from Washington Circle, c. 1920.

Cloyd Heck Marvin, President of the University, 1927-1959.

Oswald Symister Colclough, Acting President, 1959-1961, 1964-1965.

Thomas Henry Carroll, President of the University, 1961-1964.

Lloyd Hartman Elliott, President of the University, 1965-

Earl Baldwin McKinley, M.D., Dean of the School of Medicine, 1931-1938.

Walter Andrew Bloedorn, M.D., Dean of the School of Medicine, 1938-1957.

Preface

The primary purpose of this book is to trace the institutional development of medical education in George Washington University. Such a study is concerned not with the content and method of instruction but with the framework, organizational and personal, within which that instruction was carried on.

The lines along which this development is traced are set forth in the Prologue. Generally this would seem to indicate a straight chronological presentation. The reader will find, perhaps to his dismay, that this is not the case. The Medical Department was a dynamic concern. From time to time it spawned off a hospital, a dispensary, a dental school, a veterinary school, a school of pharmacy, and a training school for nurses. Although it interrupts the narrative, these institutions have to be related to the Medical Department just as the Medical Department is being constantly related to the College.

To give further value as a work of reference, biographical details are frequently inserted; so also, to give contemporary color and depth, are rather full descriptions of various incidents. Just preceding the index, which, to aid in reference, has been made very full, are lists with dates of the presidents of the University and the heads of the Medical Department. Since but little of the material is generally available, the first century, up to 1920, has been discussed in considerable depth. The memory of living men can amplify the narrative which is given for the last half-century.

In a strict sense, this is not an official history. The manuscript was seen by no one other than members of the Historian's staff before it was put into print. The author has had full access to the records of the University and he has benefited by his direct knowledge of the Medical School during a crucial period when he was Secretary of the University (1918-1929). For what appears in the book, he and he only is responsible.

It is impossible to write a book without incurring obligations on all sides. Thanks, in large measure, are due to many—to the Josiah Macy, Jr., Foundation, for a grant which assisted in the publication of this book; and, within the University, to Dr. James J. Feffer, Vice President for

Medical Affairs, Dr. Seymour Alpert, Vice President for Development, and the late Dr. John Parks for their enthusiastic encouragement, friendly interest, and generous aid; to Dean Eugene R. Magruder and Patrick A. Barbati of the College of General Studies for their very substantial assistance; to Paul Napier and Annette Steiner of Special Collections, and Isabella Young, the Medical librarian; to Marion Corddry and her associates; to Earle Newcity and his staff, who are so largely responsible for the excellence of many of the illustrations; to Kristi Brown, Editor of *G. W. Medicine;* and to David A. Dickson of the Office of Printing and Graphics. Many have gone to considerable trouble to furnish me with information from their family records; and particular thanks are due Mrs. Daniel L. Borden, Miss Edith Sewall Phillips, Elbert Staughton Wade, Louis E. Wade, and Mrs. John J. Geary. The assistance of Sister John Mary, D.C., the archivist of the Sisters of Charity at Saint Joseph's Provincial House at Emmitsburg was especially appreciated, as was that of the Reverend Joseph T. Durkin, S.J., the archivist of Georgetown University. Every page in the book gives witness to the editorial judgment, expertise, accuracy, and good taste of Dorothy Thompson; it is hard to express adequately the appreciation that is due. Donald Benton has been a constant and helpful adviser throughout the writing and publication of the volume, and David G. Wilson, Sr., and his associates of the William Byrd Press have earned genuine gratitude by the friendly and personal way in which they have produced the book.

A final word of thanks is due Ann Grier who, as editorial assistant, has seen this book through from first draft to published volume with constant care and intelligent understanding.

2023 G Street, N.W.   ELMER LOUIS KAYSER
Washington, D. C.

January 1, 1973

A·MEDICAL CENTER

Prologue

This is an account of the development of the medical department of a college in a small town on the Potomac which, in a century and a half, became the medical center of a large university in a great metropolis. While retaining its original charter, the name of the medical school and of the parent institution had been changed from time to time. Along with other variations, it had been known as the Medical Department of Columbian College in the District of Columbia; the National Medical College of Columbian University; the School of Medicine of George Washington University; and finally the Medical Center of George Washington University. It had a complicated origin and early development. It made many changes in location before coming to Washington Circle.

The Medical Department was begun as a proprietary school, with the members of the faculty totally responsible for its finances. The form and extent of that financial involvement changed with changes in the type of tenure under which the faculty occupied its quarters. Except for some periods of very brief occupancy, its instruction was given in quarters owned by the faculty, in the same quarters leased by the faculty, in a structure assigned to it by the federal government and developed into a teaching hospital with a massive increase in the cost and problems of operation, and in buildings belonging to the College. At this point, brought under the University's administrative system, the Medical School and Hospital were designed to be self-supporting. While maintenance costs ceased to be the major source of financial risk, unrealistic payments to teachers, based, as modest as they were, on the economic state of the School from year to year, constituted a continuing risk. Not until the first quarter of the present century did the adoption of a rational salary scale, the guarantee of a fixed number of professors, and the grant of an annual subsidy by the University, over and above income from tuition, remove this risk and eliminate the final vestiges of the old system. In the last half-century of its occupation of the buildings on H Street, the School of Medicine, in its development of research, its modernization of instruction, and the improvement of its facilities, laid the firm basis for the creation of a medical center.

During its first half-century, College and Medical School were located far apart. College Hill, roughly speaking, was a plot of 46½ acres, running north for a half-mile from Florida Avenue to Columbia Road, between 14th and 15th Streets. The ordinances required that the Medical Department be located in the center of the city, and so, from time to time, it was at 10th and E Streets, in Judiciary Square, and, for a century, on H Street between 13th and 14th Streets. For a brief time all the branches of the University were grouped in the same H Street area. Unfortunately, in 1910, the financial difficulties of the University caused a dispersal of its various units, only the Medical School and Hospital remaining in the old location. In 1912, the slow reassembling of those units began in Foggy Bottom with the location of the administrative offices and the Department of Arts and Sciences on G Street between 20th and 21st. The last of the units of the University to shift to the new area were the components of the Medical Center. Over a quarter of a century, beginning with the building of the Hospital and the Warwick Memorial, the units of the Medical Center were constructed in the Washington Circle area. Once again, after sixty years, the entire physical plant of George Washington University was brought together. In the University area, bounded by Pennsylvania Avenue, F Street, and 19th and 24th Streets, the Medical Center was, in accordance with its original charter, still in the heart of the city.

Changes in the size and character of the student body had been as marked as changes in the physical plant. The young man with only a preparatory school background who, in the earlier days, attended two full courses of only four months each after two or three years' study under a physician, had been succeeded by the carefully selected man or woman who had a first degree in the Arts and Sciences and who devoted full time over an equivalent of four years, with other years of postgraduate training yet to come. Or, and here he had no early parallel, he might be engaged in research, looking forward to the Ph.D. degree under the Graduate School.

Until the eve of the Civil War, the Medical Department of Columbian College was the only medical school in the District of Columbia. Its role in the life of the medical profession was a central one. The faculty encouraged and supported the foundation of many professional societies. Its lecture halls were the usual meeting places for scientific sessions and public scientific lectures. Its members were pioneers in supporting and extending the work of the Board of Health. By their own efforts and by bringing to the attention of their fellow practitioners the results of progress being made throughout the world, they raised the standards of medical practice. Their graduates not only provided in large measure for the medical needs of the District, but extended the influence of the School throughout the nation. Three of their graduates were founders of the Medical Department of Georgetown University. Responsible in large measure for the establishment of many hospitals, their first outstanding achievement in this regard was in giving to the city, through their development and maintenance of the Washington Infirmary, the first response to its need for a hospital and at the same time giving to medical education one of its earliest teaching hospitals.

PART ONE

The Beginnings
(The First Forty Years)

CHAPTER ONE

The City and The Profession

The infant city of Washington, to those who came to it as visitors or as new residents, seemed not only a city of magnificent distances but a city of unfulfilled promise. They had expected that by some strange legerdemain the new capital would immediately display evidence of monumental grandeur, commercial prosperity, and the amenities of polite living.

Included within the Federal District were two other towns, Alexandria on the Virginia side of the Potomac and Georgetown on the Maryland side, both well established and well built-up, and enjoying a considerable prosperity. In 1800, the population of the District of Columbia was 14,093. The city of Washington was located in the former Maryland territory, bounded by Rock Creek, the present-day Florida Avenue, the Eastern Branch, and the Potomac River. Georgetown's eastern boundary was Rock Creek, its northern boundary the present R Street. The part of the area not included in Georgetown and the city of Washington was known as Washington County. "The city extended from northwest to southeast about four miles and a half and from northeast to southwest about two miles and a half."[1]

There was much in the physical situation of Washington, aside from political considerations, to commend it. Its location at the confluence of two respectable streams, the Anacostia and the Potomac, seemed to insure it a promising commercial future. A naturalized citizen of Irish origin, David Warden, wrote ecstatically of its beauty:

It is scarcely possible to imagine a situation more beautiful, healthy and convenient than that of Washington. The gently undulated surface throws the water into such various directions as affords the most agreeable assemblage. The rising hills on either side of the Potomac are truly picturesque; and as the river admits the largest frigates, their sails gliding through the majestic trees which adorn its banks, complete the scenery.[2]

Man had, as yet, done but little to enhance the beauty of the area within this scenic framework that Warden so idyllically described. The land was uninteresting, for the most part old fields and commons. Its one great saving grace was to suffer quickly from the shortsightedness of man. The area was dotted with many fine stands of old forest trees, particularly white oak. The need for lumber in the many works of construction, public and private, was met by felling these trees. The extensive woods stretching from M Street north to the boundary became the "White Oak Slashes." Closer in town was a noble cluster of ancient trees around what is now 14th and G Streets. All of these trees but seven, just north of 13th and G Streets, were cut down. As a sort of memorial to what had been, these majestic survivors were enclosed and left standing for several years, to become something of a landmark as "The Seven Oaks." For the moment, the trees had served a purpose. The timber went into the buildings, the chips were gathered up for firewood, and the bark was hauled off to the tanners' vats.[3]

Ten years elapsed between the passage of the Residence Bill in 1790 and the actual location of the federal government in its new seat. The best use was hardly made of this preparatory period preceding the removal of the capital from Philadelphia to Washington. The government had attempted to establish the new city without any large expenditure of federal funds, depending for the most part on sums realized from the sale of city lots and the contributions of Maryland and Virginia. Funds came in slowly, investors were cautious, and speculators had their day. Construction, both public and private, seemed to move at a snail's pace.

Christian Hines recollected that as he stood at the little 7th Street bridge on his way to or from Georgetown in 1797, he could see, looking toward the right, "the north wing of the Capitol just rising, as it were, out of the ground." To the left was "the President's House, perhaps half a story high. These were the only public buildings then being erected." The great ceremonial highway between the Capitol and the President's house was overgrown with briars and brambles and was "almost impassable for carriages of any kind." In going down the avenue from Georgetown to the President's house, the only house that he saw, other than the Six and Seven Buildings, was an old frame house on what would now be the south side of H Street, between 18th and 19th. The Six Buildings were on the north side of the avenue between 21st and 22nd Streets. The Seven Buildings were also on the north side of the avenue beginning with 19th Street.[4] There was not a single house on Pennsylvania Avenue, between the Capitol and the President's house. "The only place that had anything like the appearance of a town or village was F Street between Fifteenth Street and St. Patrick's Church. Beyond that there were no houses except a few shanties for laborers, near Blodgett's Hotel where the General Post Office now stands, and a few scattered old frame houses on the old fields, north of F Street." Between Georgetown and the Capitol there were only three streets cut through: K Street from the lower bridge to the Six Buildings where it joined the avenue; the avenue from the Six Buildings to 15th Street, along 15th to F Street, and along F Street to St. Patrick's Church; and a road, which continued on from a little branch over E Street in a straight line on the higher ground north of the avenue to Tiber Creek, near the base of Capitol Hill. "These," says Hines, "were the only streets in Washington which were open; in fact, there were no houses to form streets." This description of the part of the city, west of the Capitol, that Hines recorded, indicates the general state of Washington just prior to the removal of the government from Philadelphia.[5]

Warden in his *Chorographical and Statistical Description*, published in 1816 on the basis of information collected a year or two previously, seems not altogether consistent in his reference to the salubrity of the District. Disclaiming as an unfounded prejudice the prevailing opinion that the climate of Washington was unhealthy, he declared that in no season the region was "visited by habitual or endemical diseases." In support of his contention, he declared that he had seen many lifelong inhabitants of the District "whose features and general appearance indicated very advanced age." He cited further evidence (although with a caveat) of a statistical nature:

Mr. Blodgett [evidently Samuel Blodgett] has, we know not from what data, estimated the annual deaths in Washington at 1 of 48 to 50 persons; in New York at 1 of 45 to 50; at Baltimore at 1 of 43 to 49; at Charleston at 1 of 35 to 40; from which it results that of all these places, Washington is the healthiest; and in this respect it has evidently an advantage over the great cities of Europe, where the annual deaths are as 1 to 23, and in towns as 1 to 28.

Some particulars that he gave rather weakened his claims as to the salubrity of the city when he listed "characteristic local ailments." In autumn bilious fever prevailed, but it was common elsewhere, he added. In winter, chronic diseases often occurred, occasioned by sudden changes in weather "which check perspiration. In July, the oppressive heat brought with it intermittent fever which seemed to originate from exhalation of marshes and borders of stagnant water. The bilious at times degenerated into a putrid fever."[6]

This is hardly a disarming description; but what could be expected in a raw city where for the first twenty years of its existence the supply of drinking water and the disposal of garbage and sewage were matters of individual arrangement?

In the light of Warden's particularized statements, rather than his general comments on health in Washington, we can understand why he devoted so much space to the medical profession in the District. In Washington, he wrote in 1816, there were nine physicians and two apothecaries who were also physicians and, in Alexandria at the same time, nine or ten physicians. Dr. Toner in his *Anniversary Oration* said that five physicians had settled in Georgetown before 1800. From the standpoint of the limited populations of the three towns, this would seem to indicate the availability of adequate professional medical attention. All of these gentlemen did not, however, devote full time to the practice of medicine. Dr. Edward Gantt of Georgetown was a minister of the Episcopal Church, and Dr. Cornelius Cunningham, a man of marked business acumen, operated a brewery near the Navy Yard.[7]

There were no regulations enforced for admission to the practice of medicine in these early years in the District. Young men desiring to enter the profession would usually study one or two years with a physician and then for one or two more years attend lectures at the colleges in Philadelphia or Baltimore. Charlatanry was by no means unknown and the preparation of many physicians fell far short of the standard. The usual fee in the city was a dollar a visit; in the country it was determined by the distance the physician had to travel. A source of added income was the sale of drugs which the physician had to carry with him in his carriage or saddlebags. Until the patient fully recovered, repeated visits were justified by the need to keep the supply of medicine from running out. Surgical cases were rare and obstetrical work was largely in the hands of old women. Warden, who was not a physician but a diplomatic agent and licensed preacher, was particularly exercised over the fact that there was no medical association in Washington for professional improvement.[8]

Dr. Toner believed that the first formal assembly of the physicians of Washington and Georgetown came in response to a call by public notice in the *National Intelligencer* of a meeting held on Thursday, April 28, 1813, at four o'clock in the Council Chamber of Washington to plan for the proper commemoration of the life and work of Dr. Benjamin Rush. Appropriate resolutions were passed at the meeting and Dr. Thomas Sim was designated to deliver a eulogy at a public meeting. The meeting was held in the Reverend Mr. Laurie's church, on the south side of F Street west of 14th Street.[9]

Four years were to pass before the physicians of Washington and Georgetown were called together at Tennison's Hotel at eleven o'clock on Friday, September 26, 1817, to consider the organization of a medical society. Sixteen physicians responded to the call and resolved "to organize at once a society in the District for the promotion of Medical Science." The meeting elected a committee of seven to draft a constitution and by-laws for the "Medical Society of the District of Columbia" for presentation at a meeting to be held on Monday, November 3. At this meeting the draft was gone over, section by section, and an adjourned session was called for November 10 for formal adoption and signature.

This organizing session was called by public advertisement to all physicians in the District (previously those from Washington and Georgetown only had been included). On January 5, 1818, the constitution and by-laws were adopted and officers for the year were elected, headed by Dr. Charles Worthington as president. According to the constitution, quarterly meetings and, when necessary, adjourned meetings were held at which papers were presented and discussed. While by general consent these meetings did bring sociability and professional enlightenment to the members, they did not drive charlatans out of practice. The Society had no sanctions to invoke against them.

In 1818, twenty-one members of the Society petitioned Congress for a charter as a medical society. Several of these petitioners were later connected with the Columbian College: Dr. Charles Worthington, Trustee, 1826-1827; Dr. Frederick May, Professor of Obstetrics, 1825-1839; Dr. Alexander McWilliams, Professor of Botany, 1824-1834; Dr. Thomas Henderson, Professor of the Theory and Practice of Medicine, 1824-1833; Dr. Nicholas W. Worthington, Professor of Materia Medica, 1824-1839.[10]

The charter was granted by Congress, and approved by President Monroe on February 16, 1819. It was almost an exact copy of the 1799 charter of the Medical and Chirurgical Faculty of Maryland. From the use of the initials "L.M.C.F." instead of the M.D. or M.B., it would appear that several of the petitioners were licentiates of the Maryland faculty only, rather than graduates of a college of medicine. Some of the twenty-one held the degree of Bachelor of Medicine (M.B.), following the British usage, since the degree of Doctor of Medicine was not generally given in this country before the early nineteenth century.

The charter declared that the petitioners and their legal successors were a body corporate under the name of the Medical Society of the District of Columbia, capable of holding real and personal property which could not exceed in total value the sum of $6,000 per annum and which could be applied only for purposes "conducive to the promoting and disseminating medical and surgical knowledge." Dates were set for four stated meetings a year. The customary officers were listed and were to be appointed regularly at the first stated meeting each year. The Society was authorized to add to its membership qualified persons engaged in the practice of medicine or surgery. An elected Medical Board of Examiners of the District of Columbia of five members, with three as a necessary quorum, was given the right to grant licenses to practice on the evidence of a full examination or diplomas "from some respectable college or society." Without such a license no one, unless previously a practitioner in the District, was to be allowed to practice medicine or surgery under penalty of a heavy fine for each offense, assessed in the county court, one-half of the fine for the treasury of the Society, the other half to the informer. Any person licensed to practice in one of the states could practice in the District.[11]

Great progress in organizing the profession in the young city had been made in a very short time. While the depths of medical ethics were yet to be plumbed in their ideal and practical aspects, a forum had been established for the discussion of scientific questions and a virtually unlimited licensing power had been established with sanctions. Until the novelty wore off, the meetings of the Society were well attended. Then the interest in the Society began rapidly to subside.

"It seems," said Dr. Toner, "the younger members and strangers settling to practice here did not speedily fraternize or endeavor to advance their own in the general interest of the profession, as the originators of the Society had done. The opening of the Medical Department of Columbian College also seems to have increased the indifference of the physicians to the interests of the Medical Society by supplying a new source of professional entertainment."[12]

The development of that "new source of professional entertainment" into a great medical center is what this book is about.

CHAPTER TWO

Opening of The Medical Department

Columbian College in the District of Columbia was chartered by an act of Congress, approved by President Monroe on February 9, 1821. The founder of the College, the Reverend Luther Rice, and his associates had hopes that the Congress would incorporate the General Convention of the Baptist Denomination in the United States, authorizing that body to hold property and to engage in various corporate activities, among which would be education. The Congress demurred at this church–state relationship and the Baptists had to look later to the legislature of Pennsylvania for incorporation of their denominational body. After much redrafting, debating, and revision in the Congress of the United States, there was granted a charter for "a college for the sole and exclusive purpose of educating youth in the District of Columbia in the English, learned and foreign languages, the liberal arts, sciences, and literature, the style and title of which shall be, and hereby is declared to be, 'The Columbian College in the District of Columbia.'" All religious tests were prohibited in no uncertain terms: "And be it further enacted, that persons of every religious denomination shall be capable of being elected trustees; nor shall any person, either as president, professor, tutor, or pupil, be refused admittance into said college, or denied any of the privileges, immunities, or advantages thereof, for or on account of his sentiments in matters of religion."[1]

Because of delays in getting favorable Congressional action, considerable progress toward opening the College had been made before the charter was granted. While the Baptist Convention had authorized the establishment of the College, it made no grant of funds to aid in its establishment or support. Instead it sent out its agents to engage in a perpetual solicitation of funds from individuals and congregational groups and societies. For $6,988, 46½ acres of land were bought, lying roughly in the area between 14th and 15th Streets, and Florida Avenue and Columbia Road. Funds were also being solicited for buildings and professorships, although the returns were meager. Plans had been made for the transfer of the Theological Institution in Philadelphia to the College in time to begin its session in September, 1821, and the College was scheduled to open its Classical Department in January, 1822.[2]

It is difficult to say just how restricted in meaning to those who wrote the charter was the expression "a college for the sole and exclusive purpose of educating youth in the District of Columbia in the English, learned and foreign languages, the liberal arts, sciences, and literature." Certainly Rice, the founder, Staughton, the first president, and their colleagues had in mind a great deal more than a mere undergraduate college of arts and sciences. They were clearly intent on developing a true university organization, quite as it would be understood today. While the transplanted Theological Department did not thrive in Washington and all but disappeared when the professor in charge, the Reverend Irah Chase, was called to establish Newton Theological Seminary in 1825, expansion along other lines was already going on.[3]

The opening of a Preparatory Department, which existed for three-quarters of a century, was authorized in 1821, and got under way at the time the College was opened. In the fall of the same year, Departments of Law and of Medicine were authorized to begin operation as soon as possible. A year later the Trustees discussed the establishment of a "Phylosophical Department and General Repository" for research, discussion, and accumulation of whatever illustrated natural history.[4]

At a meeting of the Board of Trustees held on November 24, 1821, for the main purpose of formalizing plans for the College's opening ceremonies and the inauguration of its president and professors, it was decided to establish a Medical Department in eighteen months' time. Although the actual opening of the Medical Department was still well in the future, two medical professors were elected at the same meeting and inaugurated on January 9, 1822, along with the rest of the faculty in the Classical and Theological Departments. The delay in opening the Medical Department was somewhat longer than anticipated. On September 21, 1824, after hearing letters from the two medical professors, the Trustees proceeded rapidly to the organization of the new unit. By-laws and regulations were

Luther Rice (1783-1836),
Founder of Columbian College.

The only known likeness of Rice; cut by Emily
Redd of Caroline County, Virginia, prior to 1830.
(The Virginia Baptist Historical Society.)

ADDRESS

DELIVERED

AT THE OPENING

OF THE

COLUMBIAN COLLEGE

IN THE

DISTRICT OF COLUMBIA,

JANUARY 9, 1822;

BY THE PRESIDENT,

THE REV. WILLIAM STAUGHTON, D. D.

MEMBER OF THE AMERICAN PHILOSOPHICAL SOCIETY.

WASHINGTON CITY:

PRINTED AND PUBLISHED BY ANDERSON AND MEEHAN,
COLUMBIAN OFFICE, NORTH E STREET.

1822.

Title Page of President Staughton's Inaugural.

On this occasion, Professors Sewall and J. M. Staughton were installed in their chairs, and the President announced that "additional edifices will soon be erected, where lectures will be delivered on the Institutes of Law and on Medical Science."

The Reverend William Staughton, D.D., First President of Columbian College, 1821-1827. (A portrait by Rembrandt Peale, in the University Collection.)

Thomas Sewall, M.D., Professor of Anatomy and Physiology, 1821-1839, and of Pathology, 1839-1845; First President of the Medical Faculty. (A portrait by Chester Harding in the University Collection.)

James Martin Staughton, M.D., Professor of Chemistry and Surgery, 1821-1830. (From a portrait by Anna Claypoole Peale in possession of the family.)

Joseph Borrows (1807-1889), A.B., 1825, M.D., 1828.

Circular.

THE MEDICAL DEPARTMENT
OF
The Columbian College in the District of Columbia.

THE COLUMBIAN COLLEGE in the District of Columbia, was instituted by an act of the Congress of the United States, in the winter of 1821. Soon after that period the Classical Department was brought into operation, and a course of instruction commenced. In the summer of 1824, the Medical Department was organized, and professors appointed; and in March, 1825, a course of Lectures commenced on the different branches of Medicine. The success which attended the commencement of the school, has demonstrated the peculiar advantages of its location, and inspired its friends with the fullest confidence in its utility and success.

In order to embrace all the benefits of a winter school, the Lectures will annually commence on the first Monday in November, and continue to the last of February. During this period, Lectures will be delivered daily, and full courses be given on the various branches of Medicine.

The Medical Professors are:

THOMAS SEWALL, M. D., Professor of Anatomy and Physiology.
JAMES M. STAUGHTON, M. D., Professor of Surgery.
THOMAS HENDERSON, M. D., Professor of the Theory and Practice of Medicine.
N. W. WORTHINGTON, M. D., Professor of Materia Medica.
EDWARD CUTBUSH, M. D., Professor of Chemistry.
FREDERICK MAY, M. D., Professor of Obstetrics.

Such arrangements have been made as will furnish the Professor of Anatomy with materials for demonstration, and the class with ample opportunity for the cultivation of Practical Anatomy.

Provision has also been made for exhibiting to the class the Clinical Practice and Operative Surgery, in the Infirmary of the Washington Asylum, free of expense.

The extensive and complete apparatus of the Professor of Chemistry, will afford every facility for displaying the experimental parts of that science.

The Medical College, situated in a central part of the City, about equidistant from the Capitol and President's House, is a commodious building, and well fitted up with apartments suited to the purposes of the school.

The First Printed Circular of the Medical Department.

To the Rev. Dr. Meyer from his friend & obt. Servt. Wm. Ruggles, Col. Col. D.C.

A

LECTURE,

DELIVERED AT THE

OPENING OF THE MEDICAL DEPARTMENT

OF THE

Columbian College

IN THE DISTRICT OF COLUMBIA;

March 30, 1825.

BY

THOMAS SEWALL, M. D.

PROFESSOR OF ANATOMY AND PHYSIOLOGY.

───────────

WASHINGTON CITY:

PRINTED AT THE COLUMBIAN OFFICE.

1825.

Title Page of Dr. Sewall's Address, Marking the Formal Opening of Instruction in the Medical Department.

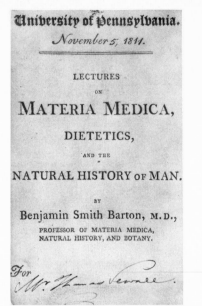

UNIVERSITY OF PENNSYLVANIA.

Nov. { 1811—12. } 14th.

LECTURES

ON

Chemistry,

BY

JOHN REDMAN COXE, M.D.

No. 242.

Mr. Thomas Sewall.

University of Pennsylvania.

November 5, 1811.

LECTURES

ON

MATERIA MEDICA,

DIETETICS,

AND THE

NATURAL HISTORY OF MAN.

BY

Benjamin Smith Barton, M.D.,

PROFESSOR OF MATERIA MEDICA,
NATURAL HISTORY, AND BOTANY.

For Mr. Thomas Sewall.

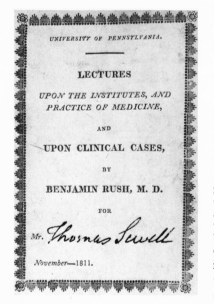

UNIVERSITY OF PENNSYLVANIA.

LECTURES

UPON THE INSTITUTES, AND
PRACTICE OF MEDICINE,

AND

UPON CLINICAL CASES,

BY

BENJAMIN RUSH, M. D.

FOR

Mr. Thomas Sewall

November—1811.

Student Cards of Thomas Sewall at the University of Pennsylvania. Although Dr. Sewall's degree was from Harvard, these cards show that he also took a full course, as was not unusual at the time, in the University of Pennsylvania. Tuition payment took the form of the purchase of such cards, each admitting to attendance at the lectures indicated. (University Collection.)

University of Pennsylvania.

Nov. 1811

LECTURES on SURGERY

by

Philip Syng Physick M.D.

and

John Syng Dorsey M.D.

For Mr. Thos. Sewall

Pennsylvania Hospital.

Thomas Sewall

Student of Doctor Barton one of the HOSPITAL PHYSICIANS, is entitled to the Privilege of attending the Practice of the House, and the Use of the Library. One Season to end first of Eleventh month Eighteen hundred Twelve

S. W. Coates

Sitting Managers.

To the Apothecary of the Hospital.

J. W. SCOTT, PRINT.

This Certificate not to be transferred or lent, under penalty of losing the Privilege.

University of Pennsylvania.

COURSE of 1811, 12.

Admit Mr. Thos. Sewall to the LECTURES ON ANATOMY.

Nov. 13. 1811

Wistar

No. 340

UNIVERSITY OF PENNSYLVANIA,

MEDICAL DEPARTMENT.

1811, 1812.

Received from Thomas Sewall A Mass.

FOUR DOLLARS for the present Session.

Edward Fox

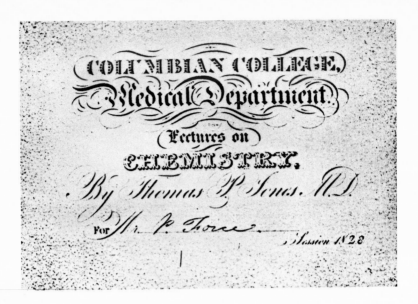

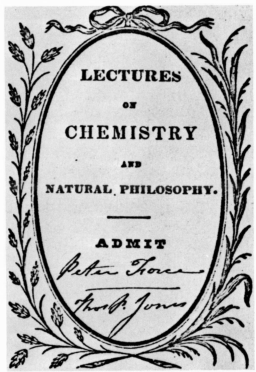

Cards for the Lectures of Dr. Thomas P. Jones (1773-1848). Dr. Jones, Professor of Chemistry, 1832-1840, was also a popular lecturer on science. Above are shown two cards of admission given to Peter Force, the archivist, the one on the bottom admitting to the doctor's popular course, the one on the top to his course at the Medical College.

adopted on October 19, fixing the last Wednesday in March, 1825, for the beginning of lectures in the Medical Department.[5]

The archives of the University offer but little information concerning the Medical Department in the first half-century of its existence, and for some periods there is practically a total blackout. Board *Minutes* are notoriously skimpy, recalling in a stark way actions taken without any full account of their sponsorship or background. Because of the limited relation of the Medical Department to the College, this was only natural. Once the Department was authorized and rules and regulations adopted, the Trustees' role was almost entirely restricted to the formal adoption of recommendations from the faculty for nominations to professorships and for the granting of the mandamus for the conferring of degrees. It would be valuable if we knew something about the discussion and debate which preceded the original action.

In his inaugural address formally opening Columbian College on January 9, 1822, the Reverend President William Staughton looked forward to the day when "additional edifices will soon be erected, where lectures will be delivered in the Institutes of Law and in Medical Science." Each of the two medical professors installed that day had important personal contacts with the College administration. Dr. Thomas Sewall was named an original Trustee in the charter and continued to serve until active participation as a professor brought him under the prohibition in the charter for a professor to serve as a Trustee. Dr. James M. Staughton was the son of the president of the College. The role of these two men in the establishment of the Medical Department was a central one. There is no mention of any action being taken by the Medical Society or any group of physicians to advance the project. Certainly the action of Congress in giving the Medical Society the sole right of licensure did put a premium on a college degree in Medicine. The only other means of establishing eligibility was by examination.

Support for the establishment of a Medical Department might well have come from lay groups in the city. We think of medical schools generally as located in populous and prosperous centers, a category in which Washington of the 1820's would hardly fall. Yet there was in the city at the time a remarkable company of men of Jeffersonian versatility. That group was large enough to produce a core of individuals of outstanding competence who joined together in 1816 to form the Columbian Institute for "the promotion of arts and sciences" with the not too unreasonable hope that their society would play a part in Washington comparable to that played by the American Philosophical Society in Philadelphia.[6]

From the sequence of events, it is evident that much time and thought went into planning for the Medical Department. As was said above, at the same meeting on November 24, 1821, when the Board decided to open a Medical Department within a year and a half, the first two professors of medicine were elected, Dr. Thomas Sewall and Dr. James M. Staughton. The latter, then only twenty-one years of age and but recently graduated from the University of Pennsylvania as a Doctor of Medicine, was asked to enter on his duties when the Department was in operation. Meanwhile he was to go to Europe and to perfect himself in the branches he would teach. The Trustees agreed to pay him up to $1,000 a year for his expenses. He was also to cooperate with Professor Alva Woods, who was being sent abroad to purchase a library, complete chemical apparatus, specimens in geology and mineralogy, and "other articles of curiosity," as well as to solicit contributions. As wise as these plans were, it seemed rather improvident for an institution just opening its doors to go into such an expensive project for full equipment when it was having to borrow $10,000 for operating expenses to get under way.[7]

In less than a month (September 21 to October 19, 1824) from the time that the Board formally began the organization of the Medical Department, by-laws and regulations were drawn up and adopted. Courses were to be held in the central part of the city. The College at the time was located just north of the boundary in what was then the county.

The branches of medicine to be taught were: anatomy and physiology, surgery, theory and practice of physic, materia medica, chemistry, and obstetrics and the diseases of women and children. The first course was to begin on the last Wednesday in March, 1825, but thereafter courses would run from the first Monday in November to the end of February. Each course was to continue from three to four months. Before a student could receive the ticket of any professor, he must pay $5 to have his name enrolled and $10 for each ticket. He could attend lectures in the Classical Department of the College without charge. Each student must attend each professor during two full courses, must have studied at least three years under some regular physician, and must be at least twenty-one years of age. If not a Bachelor of Arts, he must satisfy the faculty of his classical attainments. Thirty days before the close of his course, he must register his name with the dean and deliver an inaugural dissertation on some medical subject. All candidates must be examined by the Medical professors, with a public examination and defense of the dissertation. There was a $5 fee for the diploma and a $30 fee for the examination. Judged by the standards of the time, these requirements were high and quite in accord with the declaration of the committee on opening the College that "the course of study should not fall below the standard of institutions holding a distinguished rank among the American colleges."⁸ In the circular issued in August, 1825, fees had been increased. The charge for each ticket had been raised from $10 to $15.

As to adjuncts to teaching, it was announced that arrangements had been made to furnish the professor of anatomy with materials for demonstration and that the class would have "ample opportunity for the cultivation of practical anatomy." There would be exhibited "to the class the Clinical Practice and Operative Surgery, in the Infirmary of the Washington Asylum, free of expense. . . . The extensive and complete apparatus of the Professor of Chemistry will afford every facility for displaying the experimental parts of that science," the circular declared with complete assurance.

A later circular gave fuller detail about the building:

It is three stories high, with a spacious well-lighted and well-warmed lecture room in each story; thus allowing the students to change the rooms at the close of each lecture, and avoiding the tedium of a long confinement in the same seats. Besides the regular lecture halls and various smaller rooms for apparatus, anatomical museum, private apartments for the professors, etc., there is a capacious, well-ventilated, dissecting room, thoroughly lighted and warmed, and where, at a very moderate expense, (much less than at most medical schools), dissections are carried on during the whole session, under the immediate and constant supervision of the demonstrator, *and with the most abundant supply of material.*⁹

In a footnote the 1825 circular stated: "Good board can be obtained at from three to five dollars per week."

Lectures regularly began on the first Monday in November and continued daily until the end of February. The first course had, however, started on March 30, 1825. Dr. Toner says that this first course was given in a building located at 447 10th Street. According to the *Columbian Star* for April 9, 1825, 21 students were registered. The introductory lecture was given by Dr. Thomas Sewall, Professor of Anatomy and Physiology. It was, in many ways, a remarkable production.

He discussed reasons for delay in the cultivation of medical science in this country. "When we consider then, the object for which our ancestors immigrated to America; the difficulties they had to encounter; the state of the country to which they came; and, above all, the depressed state of medical science throughout Europe at the time, it is easy to explain their disregard to medical education and its slow progress for many years that followed."

A change came with the revival of interest in medical science in Europe, stimulated by the work of the elder Monro in Edinburgh, of William and John Hunter in London, of Boerhaave in Leyden, and of some of their French contemporaries. There were intimations as to the new advances in medical science by occasional dissection and lectures, but no organized plan was brought forward in this country until the two Philadelphians, Dr. Shippen and Dr. Morgan, graduates of the colleges at Princeton and Philadelphia respectively, and trained privately by physicians in their native city, with their studies completed in Europe, instituted the first regularly organized medical school in Philadelphia. Before long a rival school was established, but in 1791 the two were united. Students were admitted to the Pennsylvania Hospital and the Philadelphia Almshouse for clinical instruction.

From this account of the beginnings, Dr. Sewall went on to discuss briefly the history of each of the sixteen medical schools then existing, and to refer to the methods of instruction at the time and to the influence of the twenty State Medical Societies. On balance, he found the progress of the previous sixty years unrivaled anywhere. "If we have done this, in the short period of sixty years that are passed," he asked, "what will be our advance in sixty years to come?" He naturally turned to the institution which he was then inaugurating. He recalled that the founders had from the beginning had in mind a university of which a medical school would be one of its several parts. He pointed out that the age was one "when all institutions for the promotion of science, and the melioration of the conditions of man, are regarded with public favour, and sustained by a liberality of feeling known to no other age." He was impressed by the progress of the city that had risen from forest and tobacco field to bring together a population of 15,000 in a quarter of a century. He emphasized the national character of the city and the role it played as neutral ground, where young men coming from every part of the country would acquire a true national point of view, freed of sectional prejudice. All of these things gave the speaker "a confident feeling of its ultimate success," and at the end of a powerful peroration he asked: "Who knows but this school may be destined to produce a Sydenham, a Harvey, a Hunter, or a Bichat? or to give to the world a Bard, a Rush, a Warren, a Barton, or a Wistar?"[10]

The building on 10th Street near D Street used for the first two sessions was so generally unsatisfactory for medical education that the faculty moved to provide the new and efficient quarters described in the 1825 circular. A structure designed for use by the Department was erected by the faculty at the northeast corner of 10th and E Streets. The third course of lectures was given in this building, which continued to be used until 1834, "when," says Toner, "from some cause they were suspended for a few years."[11]

The August, 1825, circular of the Medical Department listed the professors as follows, it being understood that seniority would be determined by the date of appointment:

Thomas Sewall, M.D., Professor of Anatomy and Physiology
James M. Staughton, M.D., Professor of Surgery
Thomas Henderson, M.D., Professor of the Theory and Practice of Medicine
N. W. Worthington, M.D., Professor of Materia Medica
Edward Cutbush, M.D., Professor of Chemistry
Frederick May, M.D., Professor of Obstetrics

The circular was signed "Thomas Henderson, Dean." It would appear that the dean's duties primarily involved contact with students. Communications to the Trustees seem generally to have come through the senior professor, Dr. Sewall.

Thomas Sewall was descended from Henry Sewall, who emigrated to Newbury, Massachusetts, in 1635, "out of dislike to the English Hierarchy" according to Judge Samuel Sewall, his grandson. Dr. Sewall's grandfather moved to Maine where the doctor was born, April 16, 1786. He was graduated from Harvard in 1812, his class being the first to receive the degree of Doctor of Medicine from that institution. Dr. Sewall's professors' cards in the University collection show that he attended lectures at the University of Pennsylvania in 1811 and 1812. His card from the Pennsylvania Hospital entitling him "to the Privilege of attending the Practice of the House, and the Use of the Library for one season to end the first of the Eleventh month Eighteen Hundred Twelve," described him as a "Student of Doctor Barton, one of the Hospital Physicians." Included in the collection are his registration cards for 1811 and 1812, and cards for lectures on "Materia Medica, Dietetics, and the Natural History of Man" (Barton), "Anatomy" (Wistar), "Chemistry" (Coxe), "Upon the Institutes, and Practice of Medicine and Upon Clinical Cases" (Rush), and "Surgery" (Physick and Dorsey). After graduation he practiced for a few years in Essex County, Massachusetts. In 1813, he married Mary Choate, the sister of Rufus Choate. They had one child, a son, who became an eminent minister in the Methodist Church.[12]

A serious incident occurred early in Dr. Sewall's professional career that might easily have ruined him. On a snowy night in January, 1818, a light was seen moving through a cemetery in Ipswich, Massachusetts. Suspicion was heightened when a comb found on the ground there was recognized as one which had been buried with the remains of a woman recently interred. When her grave was opened, no body was found, nor were the bodies of seven others in the same cemetery found when their graves were opened. Investigation led to the discovery of the parts of three at Dr. Sewall's, who had been using them to instruct some of his students in surgery. Sewall was indicted on three counts, tried, with Daniel Webster as his counsel, and convicted on two counts, the third having been dropped on a technical objection by the defense. The eloquence and erudition of one of the leading figures of the day could not save him from being fined the formidable sum of $800. Sewall gave up his practice, but Webster prevailed upon him to come to Washington and resume his professional activity. His distinguished appearance, his influential family connections, the eminence of his sponsor, his erudition, and his ability won for him in an amazingly short time an outstanding social and professional position in the city where he was to remain for the rest of his life. He died in 1845.[13]

Dr. Thomas Sewall was undoubtedly the dominant figure in the early development of the Medical Department, a charter Trustee of Columbian College, an incorporator of the Medical Society of the District of Columbia under the second charter, one of the founders of the Medical Association of the District and of the Washington Infirmary, and a member of the Board of Health. In "The Errors of Phrenology Exposed," he entered the lists against that pseudoscience. While it is unnecessary to go into the ethical values of body-snatching for the advancement of knowledge, it must be said that, true to his puritan ancestry, there was a strong moralistic element in Sewall's makeup. This was clearly indicated in his charge to the graduates at the 1827 Commencement of the Medical Department.[14]

There were 6 graduates in the first class in 1826: Richard Angel (England), James Cooke (Maryland), Jesse Ewell (Virginia), Charles K. Laub (District of Columbia), Thomas J. Moore (District of Columbia), and Charles H. Stone (District of Columbia). In the second class (1827), there were 8 graduates: Thomas Evans (Maryland), James Hogan (Ireland), Henry King (District of Columbia), Robert Kirkwood (Maryland), John G. Stanhope (Virginia), William L. Wharton (District of Columbia), Richard Wheat (Virginia), and Benjamin F. Wing (Massachusetts). Graduating classes remained about this size during the first thirty years.[15]

In accordance with a regulation of the Trustees, at each Medical Commencement the president of the College was required to deliver a charge to the graduating class upon the subject of their moral deportment, and the dean of the Medical faculty was required to deliver an address upon the subject of their professional conduct.

In the president's address to the candidates for the degree in Medicine at the Commencement of March 16, 1826, the Reverend Dr. Staughton urged the graduates to be good Samaritans. He quoted with warm approbation the words of Dr. Rush, "I esteem the poor my most profitable patients, for God is their pay-master." He warned them that they would find occasions for vexation. "Suffer," he said, "no such occurrence to depress your spirits, much less to arouse indignant passions. We can do no other than take human nature as it presents itself."

In his charge delivered to the graduating class on March 22, 1827, Dr. Sewall seems to have discharged the duties of both president and dean; for President Staughton at the time was in Charleston, frustrated, embarrassed, and deeply wounded by the disquieting news about a crisis in the College that had come to him. He was on the point of resigning. His resignation was dated on the day following Commencement, March 23, 1827. In his address, Dr. Sewall, in words of great solemnity, tried to impress upon the graduates the gravity of the responsibilities they were about to assume. Before he placed in their hands "the parchment roll which you are about to bear away as the evidence of your attainments and of our confidence in your skill," he wanted to emphasize the moral duties of the medical profession. He listed and discussed eight moral principles:

1. Maintain, gentlemen, a sacred regard to truth.
2. Be attentive to the sufferings of the poor.
3. In your professional intercourse, assiduously cultivate a *pure* and *elevated* style of conversation, *certainty* and *gentleness* of manner, and kindness of heart.
4. Maintain a due observance of the Sabbath.
5. Be guarded against Infidel sentiments.
6. Observe strict temperance in the use of ardent spirit.
7. Intimately connected with intemperance, is the practice of gambling. Let me exhort you, gentlemen, to abstain from all games of chance.
8. Discountenance and abstain from the practice of duelling.

In summary he urged each of them ever to keep in view the moral obligation he was under to his patients and to the community, so that when he passed away after a life of dedicated service, the traveler who passes by will point to his tomb and say, "There lies the dust of an honest man, one who loved truth, was just to the poor, was pure, kind, and courteous, revered the Sabbath, discountenanced infidelity, reproved drunkenness, gambling, and duelling, and practiced and enforced all the moral virtues."[16]

In his charge to the class of 1827, Dr. Sewall laid great emphasis on the importance of temperance in the use of alcohol. "There is no subject, gentlemen, on which I would entreat you with more earnestness than this." He is one of the outstanding figures in the temperance movement in this country.

J. C. Furnas, in his popular and highly entertaining book *The Life and Times of the Late Demon Rum*, wrote that in 1831 the Reverend Dr. Edwards, Federalist record and all, was invited to address a Democrat-dominated Congress on the curse of rum. Shortly thereafter, with very distinguished sponsorship, the Reverend John Marsh of the Baltimore Temperance Society organized a great Temperance meeting in Washington, and in the following year under much the same patronage formed a Congressional Temperance Society for the encouragement of sentiment against the sale and use of liquor. At the first meeting of this organization Dr. Sewall was a speaker.[17]

Before the events cited by Furnas, Dr. Sewall was already recognized as an authority on the subject of the physical effects of intemperance. On

November 15, 1830, he delivered an address before the Washington City Temperance Society, which was published and distributed by the Society. In his lecture, after outlining the physical and spiritual effects of alcohol, he urged his hearers to "spread abroad information upon the subject of intemperance, to rouse up the people to a sense of their danger, and to form temperance societies." He urged especially that the women of the country recognize their duty and make men "swear eternal hatred to ardent spirit."[18]

This lecture is described as "for years one of the standard works on the question." Although Dr. Sewall wrote and lectured widely, his work in this field, which was most influential because it backed up his fervor for temperance with his distinction as a pathologist, was a series of charts, in color, which showed vividly the effects of alcohol on the human body. Used again and again as illustrations for lectures and temperance tracts, these charts served as a basis for the scientific attack on the use of alcohol. Science, in his mouth, spoke with magisterial authority:

Alcohol is a poison, forever at war with man's nature; and in all its forms and degrees of strength produces irritation of the stomach which is liable to result in inflammation, ulceration, and mortification; a thickening and induration of its coats, and finally schirrus, cancer, and other organic affectations. It may be asserted with confidence that no one who indulges habitually in the use of alcoholic drinks, whether in the form of wine or more ardent spirits, possesses a healthy stomach.

The vividness of Dr. Sewall's language made the macabre and feeble color of his charts look even paler. Furnas refers to these charts as "allegedly based on Dr. William Beaumont's studies on what went on inside a patient with a never-healing hole in his stomach." He is undoubtedly referring to the case of Alexis St. Martin, the Canadian half-breed, with whom Beaumont, an Army surgeon, began to work in 1825 on the island of Mackinaw, eventually bringing him 2,000 miles to Plattsburg, New York, to complete his observations and studies. Beaumont published his *Experiments and Observations* in 1833. He had no degree in Medicine but in that same year Columbian conferred upon him the degree of Doctor of Medicine, *honoris causa*. Sewall's "Diagrams of the Human Stomach in Various Conditions" was first published in 1842. Chronology as well as subject matter would seem to reinforce the suggestion, repeated by Furnas.[19]

Dr. Sewall held the chairs of anatomy and physiology from 1821 to

1839 and of pathology from 1839 until his death in 1845. No one contributed as fully as he to the organization, development, and prestige of the Medical Department in its first two decades.

Ranking next to Dr. Sewall in the order of appointment to the first faculty was Dr. James M. Staughton, the young son of the president of the College. Born in 1800 in Bordentown, New Jersey, he received his A.B. in 1818 and his M.D. in 1821 from the University of Pennsylvania, and an A.M. from Princeton in 1821. In the same year he was elected professor of chemistry and surgery in the Medical Department of Columbian College, then projected but not to offer instruction for three years. Dr. Staughton was directed to proceed to Europe, there to study methods of medical education and to perfect himself in the branches that he was to teach. He had the additional tasks of helping his colleague, Professor Woods of the Classical Department, acquire a library and scientific apparatus. His father, the reverend president, was quite solicitous about him during his two-year sojourn abroad and plied him generously with good advice. English by birth, the father was delighted with the warm hospitality extended to his son while abroad by distinguished public men and important clergymen and figures in the world of learning. The young Staughton was enjoined to make frequent memoranda on things that caught his interest: "to speak boldly in France all the French you know," and to refrain from too much walking, so as not to hinder his health and his studies. He returned from Europe in the fall of 1823.

His tour had been an extensive one. Landing at Liverpool and paying some attention to its public institutions, he had gone on to London for an extended stay devoted to visiting hospitals and museums and attending lectures. Then he went on to Oxford and Cambridge. In both universities he was treated with great consideration, but his stay in Oxford was particularly valuable because of the many kindnesses of the professor of chemistry. His travels on the Continent began in disappointment, for the day before his arrival in Paris the police had closed the School of Medicine because of student rioting. When he found that the scientific courses at the Sorbonne had not been interrupted he enrolled at once. Whatever additional time he had was devoted to visiting hospitals and museums, the Jardin des Plantes, and the Collège de France. He was particularly interested in the fact that these institutions were government-supported and, hence, that poverty did not impede "the progress of youth in the paths of science." After five months in Paris, he attended lectures at the School of Medicine, which had been allowed to reopen. Returning to

London and stopping on the way only to visit hospitals in Amsterdam and the University of Leyden, after a brief stay he went on to Edinburgh, where he spent considerable time. Visiting New Lanark and Glasgow, and hurriedly touring the Highlands, he returned to Liverpool, where he boarded ship for Philadelphia. Such was the Grand Tour that the Trustees' wisdom and subsidy made possible for the young professor of medicine.[20]

In the course of his practice in Washington, Dr. Staughton is said to have been the first in the city to operate successfully for stone in the bladder.[21]

Dr. Staughton resigned his professorship in 1830 to move to Cincinnati at the strong urging of Supreme Court Justice John McLean of Ohio. He became professor of surgery in the Medical College of Ohio, which had been founded in 1818 and reorganized in 1824-1825. In Cincinnati he quickly gained prominence, which was greatly enhanced by his popular experimental scientific lectures in the Lyceum and Mechanics Institute and by his devotion to the patients in the Commercial Hospital and Almshouse. He died August 6, 1833, in the course of a raging epidemic, according to the family tradition, from fatigue and exposure in the pursuit of his professional duties. Staughton died at the early age of thirty-three, before the great promise that he had given from his youth could be completely fulfilled. Before he received his degree he taught at a young women's seminary then headed by his father. While a student in the Philadelphia Almshouse his insistence upon attending to duties almost cost his life in a typhus fever epidemic. Years later in Cincinnati, he was not so fortunate. Distinguished, even handsome in appearance, socially gifted, and outstanding intellectually, James Staughton in a brief career attained marked eminence.[22]

Dr. Thomas Henderson, Professor of the Theory and Practice of Medicine, "who had all the pomp of a professor," was the third in order of seniority of the first Medical faculty. Born in 1789 in Dumfries, Virginia, he received his degree of Doctor of Medicine from the University of Pennsylvania in 1809. He was the brother of Colonel Archibald Henderson of Marine Corps fame, and the husband of Anne, the daughter of Commodore Thomas Truxtun, U.S.N. Dr. Henderson was one of the original incorporators of the Medical Society of the District of Columbia. Elected in 1824, he resigned his chair in 1833 to accept a commission as Assistant Surgeon, United States Army, and was assigned to duty at West Point. His career in the military service was one of great distinction. It was on the basis of his recommendations that the Medical Corps was reorganized in 1834. A series of his letters addressed to George Bancroft, Secretary of the Navy, and published in the *National Intelligencer* in 1845 over the pseudonym "Washington" has been given credit for stirring up public support for the establishment of the Naval Academy at Annapolis. While professor of the theory and practice of medicine, he published a translation of Bichat's *Human Pathology* (Philadelphia, 1829). He died in 1854. "As a professional man," says Busey, "few enjoyed a higher reputation."[23]

Dr. Nicholas William Worthington, Professor of Materia Medica, was an incorporator of the Medical Society of the District of Columbia under both of its charters. He was the son of Dr. Charles Worthington (1759-1836), who was a founder of the Society and its first president and also was a founder of the Medical and Chirurgical Faculty of Maryland. The younger Worthington was born in Maryland in 1789 and received the degree of Doctor of Medicine from the University of Pennsylvania in 1815. Elected professor of materia medica in 1824, he resigned his chair in 1839 because of ill health; he died at Brentwood in 1849. He is described as "a man of character and refinement, the pink of politeness, bashful and modest as a girl."[24]

When Dr. James M. Staughton resigned in 1825 as professor of chemistry to give his full attention to the chair of surgery, he was succeeded by Dr. Edward Cutbush (1772-1845), a native of Pennsylvania and student of Dr. Benjamin Rush, who received his degree of Doctor of Medicine from the University of Pennsylvania in 1794. Dr. Cutbush, a surgeon in the United States Navy (1799-1820), held the chair of chemistry for only two years. He was "a high-toned gentleman" who retired from the Navy when Andrew Jackson was inaugurated President.[25]

Dr. Frederick May was born in Boston in 1773 and received the degree of Bachelor of Medicine from Harvard in 1795. Elected professor of obstetrics in 1825, he served until 1839. Dr. May was an incorporator of the Medical Society under both of its charters and president of the Medical Association of the District of Columbia (1833-1848). He was a member of the first Board of Health in the District. Coming to Washington in 1795, he was considered with the elder Worthington as standing in the front rank of his profession in the early decades of the past century. He is supposed to have told Dr. Alexander McWilliams of regret at his entering upon the practice of medicine in Washington after his retirement from the Navy because there was no more business here than May could conveniently handle. "Frederick May," wrote Dr. Busey, "was a scholarly man and an erudite physician, a ready and fluent lecturer; and during the greater part of his long life commanded an enormous business." He died in 1847. Dr. May's professional associates seem to have been equally impressed with the distinction of his lineage, his dramatic ability as a lecturer, and the extent of his "business."[26]

These six men composed the first faculty of the Medical Department. They were all successful physicians with high social standing, and several of them had at some time had connection with the armed forces. All had professional degrees, four from the University of Pennsylvania and two from Harvard. Collecting as fully as he could at the time of his *Anniversary Oration* in 1866, Dr. Toner listed the publications of the early medical men in the District of Columbia. He listed eight publications by Cutbush, ten by Henderson, ten by Sewall, two by Staughton, and two by Nicholas Worthington. None was listed for May, although elsewhere he is credited with a publication in the *Boston Medical and Surgical Journal*, 1847. Considering the time and the obvious incompleteness of the list, the showing is highly creditable.

Joseph Borrows (1807-1889), A.B. 1825, M.D. 1828, the close friend of Dr. James M. Staughton, the classmate of Harvey Lindsly, later a president of the American Medical Association, spoke before the Medical Society on his recollections of fifty-five years of professional life. He entered Columbian College as a freshman in 1822 and as an undergraduate in the College heard lectures by Thomas Sewall, J. M. Staughton, and Alexander McWilliams, who were then lecturing in the Classical Department. Interested at first only in a liberal education, he was so impressed by the lectures of these gentlemen that when the Medical Department opened he entered, fully determined to become a physician. Borrow's is but one of the testimonials to the appealing personality, the human qualities, and the high scholarship of these early teachers. After fifty-five years, they were still giants in his sight.[27]

CHAPTER THREE

The First Decade

In the years when the first classes were being graduated, both the College and its Medical Department had to face challenges. In the case of the former they were financial with personal overtones; in the latter, legal with professional overtones.

Columbian College came into being under the sponsorship of the Baptist Convention, which indirectly controlled elections to the Board of Trustees, received regular reports from its officers, and discussed and expressed judgments on its policies. It did not give the College a lump sum for endowment, nor did it vote subsidies. It commissioned agents to carry on a continuous solicitation of the Baptist community and friends of the College throughout the states for donations which were turned over to the College. These funds were raised in various ways: gifts from individuals, congregations, and organizations; collections taken up at meetings; sale of so-called "stocks"; and "scholarships" authorizing the donor to name student beneficiaries. To these funds were added payments for tuition. With these moneys the Trustees had to pay instructional costs, reduce the college debt, maintain the property, and provide for expansion. Funds paid for student boarding, lodging, and other living expenses were collected and disbursed by the steward who, after all of the costs of his department had been met, retained the unexpended balance from his collections as compensation. To make any estimate of income for budgeting purposes was totally impossible. Collections by the agents and other donations vacillated from year to year and the yield from tuition fees was unpredictable. Because of the "scholarship" system many fees had been paid in advance at a reduced rate and did not add to current income. Indigent students were treated with great generosity and candidates for the ministry often paid nothing at all.

Painful surprise was exhibited when, after five years of operation, the College was found to be $50,000 in debt and without means to pay current expenses. This discovery, which should not have been unexpected, triggered an unfortunate chain of events. The Baptist Convention, in alarm, asserted for its own protection that it was not responsible for the financial affairs of the College. Luther Rice, who as treasurer and agent, was an official of both the College and the Convention, was singled out as the scapegoat and condemned publicly both for poor business methods and, although completely absolved later, for irregularities in the handling of the institution's finances. There was a rush of faculty resignations, student morale was shattered, and patrons were confused. President Staughton and several Trustees resigned. To allow time for reforming its ranks, the College declared an extended vacation, and a group of influential friends of the College in the Convention formed an emergency committee which formulated the plan that eventually restored the College to solvency.[1]

The bitter ordeal that Luther Rice, the founder of the College, had to undergo in this period of stress was unfortunate and undeserved. At the same time it was understandable. He was completely selfless but he was as strong-willed as he was unsystematic. So dear was the College to him that he perhaps was too insistent upon doing too many things for it. Because of this tendency of Rice and inertia on the part of others, the whole burden of financing fell almost completely upon him. Trying to be at the College often enough to advise in educational matters (and he had vision here) and at the same time to travel up and down the eastern seaboard and even into the Middle West collecting for the College, for religious periodicals and publications, and for missions, he could hardly be expected to keep orderly accounts. His *Journal* in which he made daily entries served as both diary and account book. The jumble of personal data, amounts received and disbursed, along with anything else that he cared to recall presented an all but impossible task for anyone to unscramble. Rice himself resisted militantly having to take time off to make up financial statements when he thought there were other much more important things to be done. Bitter misunderstanding, much of it undeserved, was the price he had to pay for his belief that it was more important to go out after money than to take time to make systematic records and reports on its receipt and expenditure.[2]

The Medical Department was not materially involved in the financial woes of the mother institution unless the College's distress lowered its prestige and made it vulnerable. It enjoyed financial autonomy, independent of the College, with all risk being taken by the Medical faculty. That faculty had troubles of its own.

Dr. Toner in his frequently quoted *Anniversary Oration* (1866) wrote that "in 1825 and 1826, during a period of the most active discontent among the members of the Medical Society of the District of Columbia, a very determined effort was made by a few physicians of Washington and Georgetown to form a new medical society, which should supersede the chartered organization." The formidable nature of the schismatic movement was shown when at the meeting on April 6, 1826, of those who had agreed to form a new medical association Dr. May was elected chairman and Dr. Henderson secretary. These men were both highly influential physicians and members of the Medical faculty. Two more meetings were held within a week. The purpose of the meetings was never realized, but they did unfortunately tend to polarize existing opinions. Two years later, on January 23, 1828, the Medical Society of the District of Columbia did meet to decide "whether the Society shall in future hold its sittings." The Society did not agree to dissolve.

In this period of uncertain allegiance to the Medical Society of the District of Columbia, the professors and students of the Medical Department of Columbian College organized, in 1826, the Washington Medical Society. Limited at first to its own group of students and professors, the Society later admitted local practitioners. Meetings were held in the Medical School. The president of the Society was a professor, all the other officers students. At graduation students became honorary members. An elected Board of Examiners, each member representing one division of the science as then taught, recapitulated lectures and conducted quizzes on the subjects within each branch. The meetings were fully attended not only by students but also by practitioners because of the highly instructive character of the lectures and demonstrations. The Society did not meet after 1832.

The indifference of some and the hostility of other members to the Medical Society of the District of Columbia was shown not only by a willingness to discuss its dissolution but by failure to attend its meetings. Lack of a quorum is said to have prevented the election of officers in 1831, 1832, and 1833. Perhaps the cholera epidemic of 1832 was partially responsible. When a revival of better feeling led to the holding of regular meetings and the election of officers, the Medical Society learned rather dramatically that its charter had been forfeited by its failure to elect officers and that it had therefore no legal existence.

A certain John Williams, an oculist who had practiced and received fees but was not licensed by the Medical Society's Board of Examiners, was charged with practicing medicine without a license, a specific violation on December 15, 1836, being cited. The defense claimed that since the Society had not held annual meetings for some years before, the charter had lapsed. The Medical Board had, therefore, never been legally elected and hence had no power of licensure or right to prosecute. Taking advantage of wide dissensions in the medical community, the defense ranged high and wide: some alleged members claimed that they no longer belonged, that there had been an agreement that the assets of the Society would be divided among the members; the *Minutes* of the Board had been lost. With Chief Justice Cranch of the Circuit Court of the United States presiding, the case was presented with great fullness. The jury, after being out for two days and a night, brought in a verdict of "not guilty."

Under these circumstances the Society had to petition the Congress for a renewal of the charter with amendments. The second charter, in the main following closely the original charter, was approved by President Van Buren July 7, 1838.[3]

It was in a period of confusion within the organized profession that the Medical Department of Columbian College was severely challenged. On February 13, 1826, the Senate of the United States (19th Congress, 1st Session) ordered printed a *Memorial by Sundry Citizens of the District of Columbia, praying That a Charter may be granted by Congress to enable them to institute a Medical College, etc.* The petition was signed by thirty-eight of the leading citizens of Washington, with the name of General John P. Van Ness heading the list. At least eight of the signers were physicians.

Although the second course of lectures in the Medical Department was being completed at the time, there was no mention of Columbian in the petition. The memorialists took a *pro bono publico* stance. The time had come when a well regulated Medical College should be started in the city. They concluded their memorial "by the assurance that the desire to see medical instruction originated upon a broad, liberal, and dignified basis, one worthy of the Capital of the American People, is the sole motive of your petitioners."

On the same day, February 13, 1826, the Senate ordered printed a *Memorial of the Professors in the Medical Department of the Columbian College in the District of Columbia* signed by Thomas Sewall, Chairman, and Thomas Henderson, Secretary, for the faculty.

The faculty pointed out that the Medical Department existed by the authority of the Congressional charter of Columbian College, that it was fully organized and suitably staffed, and that the second course, with a class of 30 pupils, was about completed. It was pointed out that the Trustees had given nothing more than the power to confer degrees, that all else was at the personal risk of the faculty. The first building used being found inadequate, the faculty on their own responsibility had raised $6,000 to build a large and adequate structure. They pointed out the difficulties that had arisen previously when more than one school had been started in the same city.

In this city, the medical professors have personally, unaided by the Trustees, at their own risk, pledged themselves to give to their school that dignity and character which shall render it worthy of its origin in The Congress of the United States, and of its location. No monopoly is here aimed at; nothing unworthy of the high spirit of professional liberality.

A week later, on February 20, 1826, the Senate ordered printed a *Counter Memorial of Sundry Citizens of the District of Columbia praying That a Charter may be granted by Congress to enable them to institute a Medical College, etc.*" This document was signed by Thomas Sim, Henry Huntt, and Thomas Randall, the committee on behalf of the original memorialists. Of the three, only Huntt's name appeared among the original signers. Dr. Sim was a physician of considerable distinction, a graduate of the University of Pennsylvania. The mild objectivity, the freedom from personal rancor which distinguished the original memorial and the faculty's reply had now totally disappeared. The distinguished citizens of Washington had apparently retreated from what was obviously a professional squabble.

The committee of three alleged that the Medical Department of Columbian had no standing in law, that the charter of 1821 from which it allegedly derived its authority established only a college and limited it to the conferring of degrees in the Arts and Sciences. They discussed at great length the meaning of "college" and "university," drawing upon the history of Georgetown College to sustain their position.

Founded in 1789 by virtue of a law of Maryland, the degree-granting powers of Georgetown College were conferred upon it by an act of Congress in its charter of 1815, six years before the Columbian charter was granted. In contrast to the very full Columbian charter of 1821, the Georgetown charter of 1815 was very brief, being primarily an authorization to grant degrees "in the faculties, arts, sciences, and liberal professions, to which persons are usually admitted in other Colleges or Universities in the United States." The committee emphasized the significance of the fuller enumeration of areas in which degrees could be granted, and the inclusion of the words "or Universities." It was contended that if Congress had intended powers of similar latitude for Columbian to those granted Georgetown six years before, it would have been so stated.

The countermemorialists contended that Columbian claimed "the exclusive consideration of Congress" because they had undertaken personal responsibilities and made large expenditures and because they had successfully "filled the professorship from the medical faculty of the District." This, said the committee, proved nothing. In any but an endowed medical school, professors always have to take these risks; and, if permitted, the memorialists "are ready and willing to incur to a much greater extent, and they modestly hope to a more effectual purpose," the same risks. Not only, they contended, is the department illegal in its creation and its acts null and void:

but it must also be apparent, from the history of this medical school as given by its professors, from its location in this city, apart from, irresponsible to, and with no regular nutriment or support from the parent institution, that it is a mean excrescence on that body, a carnal adoption, and not a legitimate member of the family.

As to the second point, the countermemorialists accepted the Columbian professors' appraisals of themselves, until time tested their correctness. They realized that they had been anticipated in their attempt to establish a medical school and they would never have raised any difficulties "if they had been permitted by that institution to proceed without molestation and opposition in the fair legal acquisition of their project."

The fourth pamphlet on the subject was printed by order of the Senate on February 22, 1826—a *Memorial of Sundry Citizens of the District of Columbia praying that another Medical College may not be incorporated in the City of Washington.* It was a brief statement asking that the District be spared the injurious effects of rivalry and division by the incorporation of a new medical college and expressing the view that the present institution was adequate to the exigencies of the profession and community. It was signed, along with many others, by thirteen physicians, none of them members of the Columbian faculty. The more than one hundred signers included practically all of the most distinguished Washingtonians of the time, such men as Peter Force, Colonel Archibald Henderson, Thomas Law, Gales and Seaton, the printers, Judge William Cranch, Thomas Peter, Francis Scott Key, the Reverend Stephen Balch, and the Reverend James Laurie.

Another medical school was not chartered at this time. What was the meaning of these memorials to the Congress of the United States? An answer can only be ventured on the basis of supposition. Unfortunately the *Minutes* of the Medical faculty are missing for the period through 1838, the earliest volume of the *Dean's Book* begins with 1839, the Board of Trustees' *Minutes* yield nothing, and the press just as little. Professional reticence and a sense of delicacy might account for the lack of much information; but the four documents, printed by the Senate's order and showing the signatures, pro and con, of most of the practitioners in the District and of a hundred leading citizens, would seem to indicate that the matter was one of general knowledge. From bits of information scattered through the numerous pages of Dr. Busey's writings, some observations of his own, and some gleaned from Toner's *Oration*, it would seem that support of the Medical Society by its members was at a low ebb as shown by the lack of quorums at stated and annual meetings, and that there was considerable hostility among the members themselves. Writing retrospectively, Dr. Busey commented that "it was not long after coming here that I discovered that the profession was not a harmonious fraternity." It certainly was not in the late 1820's and early '30's. Toner wrote that the years 1825 and 1826 were a period of the most active discontent among the members of the Medical Society of the District of Columbia and that a determined effort was made to establish a new society at a meeting called for April 6, 1826.[4]

The Medical Society of the District of Columbia owed its origin in large measure to the desire of local physicians to rid the District of charlatans who, without adequate training or professional restraints, were foisting themselves on the people. Accordingly, the Society's original charter of 1819 and the renewed and revised charter of 1839 had as their major significance the establishment of a procedure for licensure, with sanctions to enforce its observance.[5]

The second great problem with which the profession had to deal was centered in its own midst. The practice of medicine in the District had become a highly competitive business. Questions concerning ethics and fees were constantly arising. Though the language differed, Section 4 in both the first and second charters carefully and specifically excluded, from the powers granted, the right to establish or enforce a tariff of charges for medical attendance or advice. Section 1 in both charters limited the Society to promoting and disseminating medical knowledge; "no other purpose whatever" was permitted. Some regulation seemed indicated. There was a belief that some physicians solicited patients with moderate fees as an inducement, that some were lax in enforcing payment or were even rendering gratuitous services. In Georgetown there had existed the custom of receiving an annual fixed payment, covering all of the services rendered to a family or individuals. A meeting was set for January 4, 1833. It was not advertised as was the usual custom, but physicians in Washington were called upon individually and asked to be present. As a result of a second meeting, called three days later, a committee drafted a system of ethics and a fee bill to which practitioners were asked to subscribe. These subscribers became members of the Medical Association of the District of Columbia when the physicians of Georgetown subscribed to the principles adopted and became members of the Association.[6]

During this period of disquiet within the profession, the memorials and countermemorials were laid before Congress. Looking at the documents themselves, the first seemed clearly a petition for a charter for a medical school. The fair assumption was that it would be simply a medical school, chartered as such, and standing independently. The national legislature would do for the capital what state legislatures had done for their states. The memorial was not highly argumentative in tone. The faculty's rejoinder was more argumentative since it examined the first memorial in some depth. Its position was that there was a Medical Department in being, legally and actually, and another was unnecessary.

The second memorial of those seeking a charter for a new medical school, or the countermemorial, is highly argumentative in refutation of the faculty's position, point by point, employing a uniform tone of denigration. The final memorial with more than one hundred signatures briefly reemphasized the faculty's position without argument or details.

The so-called countermemorial deserves special comment. The description of College and University was interesting historically, if not totally accurate as to usage in this country. The exact extent of the grant of powers was clearly arguable. The contention of the counter-memorialists that the Columbian professors had tried "to establish their claim to the exclusive consideration of Congress" was not supported by anything in the faculty's memorial. The faculty did not assert that Congress could not grant another charter, but that it should not because it was unnecessary.

The argument based on the location of the Medical School in the city, apart from the parent institution, was specious since the charter of 1821 fixed the District of Columbia as the seat of the institution. Though the Medical Department operated in the city of Washington and the College in the county, both city and county were parts of the District.

Finally the charge that the Medical faculty sought to maintain a monopoly was fully disproved by their own statement. If a second medical school was desired at the time, Georgetown's charter of 1815, which they referred to so fully, would have certainly permitted the organization of a medical department under the aegis of that ancient institution.

In the Georgetown (D.C.) *Metropolitan* for March 25, 1826, a very interesting letter to the editor, signed "Civis," appeared with reference to the controversy. The writer was thoroughly conversant with the documents. In places the paraphrase is very close, with usually some comments of the writer thrown in. Civis declared that it was well known to most of the citizens of the District that the oldest practicing physicians in Washington had contemplated the establishment of a medical school long before 1821, but had "deferred to a more auspicious period" because the sparseness of the population would make difficult the securing of material for the anatomical branch. That these gentlemen were surprised, as Civis said, when the Medical Department of Columbian was started is strange. The intention of the Trustees had been announced in 1821 and frequent mention of preparatory steps being taken had appeared in the public prints. It would not be surprising if Civis himself was one of the memorialists.[7]

The effects on the Medical Department of Columbian of the abortive effort to obtain a charter for a new medical school and of the general disquiet within the profession itself are hard to pinpoint. Dr. Toner stated in his *Anniversary Oration* in 1866 that "from some cause" lectures were suspended in 1834 and not resumed until a general reorganization in 1839. What was unknown to Dr. Toner more than a century ago is still unknown. The list of professors with the years of their tenure, prepared by Dean Hodgkins eighty years ago, shows no lapse of appointments that would suggest unusual displacement of faculty members. In fact, on April 27, 1836, the Trustees, in their usual fashion, elected for regular three-year terms the professors of anatomy and physiology (Sewall), materia medica and botany (N. W. Worthington), obstetrics (F. May), and surgery (Hall).[8]

A normal number of medical graduates is shown for the years immediately preceding the suspension: 11 in 1830; 10 in 1831; 9 in 1832; 8 in 1833; and 9 in 1834, 9 being the average size of graduating classes from the beginning. However, the College had but a single graduate in 1834 in the Arts and Sciences and no public Commencement was held.[9]

That the Medical School had been enjoying at least a fair measure of prosperity seemed to be indicated by a circular that appeared in the *Washington City Chronicle* on January 31, 1829, under the signature of "James M. Staughton, M.D., Dean" and dated January 24, 1829. Preceding the circular was a paragraph of editorial comment commending the circular "to the attention of our readers" and expressing high praise "for this act of philanthropy" extending the benefits of medical education to those lacking means. The circular stated that the School would admit "one student of the character contemplated from each of the Territories, to attend all the lectures without charge." The only financial charge would be $5 for graduation. The offer was repeated in the circulars of later years.[10]

On March 14 of the same year, the Commencement of the Medical Department was the occasion for the formal inauguration of the Reverend Stephen Chapin as second president of the College. Just before the beginning of the 1829-1830 session a notice in the *Columbian Gazette*, signed by "Thomas P. Jones, M.D., Dean," announced that the lectures introductory to the medical course would commence on Monday, November 2, at noon. A lecture on each of six branches was scheduled for that week, Monday through Saturday. "The physicians of the District and the friends of Science generally are invited to attend." This invitation, characteristic of courses both in the College and in medicine, was not taken as purely formal, but very generally accepted by interested townspeople. John Quincy Adams was a frequent attendant.[11]

In addition to lectures in regular courses for degree candidates, lecture series designed for the public were frequently arranged by members of the faculty and visiting experts. We find, for example, an advertisement in *The Globe* announcing "Lectures on Chemistry and on the auxiliary branches of science" by Dr. Thomas P. Jones, Professor of Chemistry, who was serving as dean. The lectures were to run from December through February, every Monday, Wednesday, and Friday from 5 to 6 P.M. The charge was: "Tickets for the course to gentlemen, not members of the medical class—$10; to ladies—$5. Family tickets on liberal terms." The lecturer promised that the principles of his subject and "of the auxiliary branches of science" would be "familiarly explained," and "the whole illustrated by numerous and appropriate experiments."[12]

This type of extracurricular activity was quite common at the time. Many found the job of itinerant lecturer more attractive than the professional task. So it was apparently with Dr. Jones when he came to announce his farewell series. He had now improved his sales technique. He promised "a great number of brilliant and striking experiments." His aim was "to pursue the truths of science in a style of the utmost familiarity and perspicuity, and to impress them upon the mind by the most appropriate and obvious displays." A $10 ticket now carried with it "the privilege of bringing a lady." Otherwise the charge was $5 for ladies, or youths. The introductory lecture at noon on Thursday, November 6, 1833, was free! His advertisement announced that he had determined to retire from the chair of chemistry in the Columbian College at the close of this course, his other avocations "rendering the fulfillment of its duties too laborious." In 1839, Dr. Jones was back as professor of chemistry and pharmacy. The short time that he continued on the faculty was rendered difficult by a series of arguments with his colleagues arising out of conflicts of interest in the dual role of professor and public lecturer that he elected to play.[13]

Thomas P. Jones (1773 or 1774-1848), an Englishman by birth, was in many ways a remarkable man. Alternating periods of lecturing with teaching, he achieved considerable prominence from his success as editor for twenty-three years of the Franklin Institute's *Journal* which he made the leading news medium for inventors and engineers, from his service as superintendent of the United States Patent Office, from authoritative works on chemistry, and from his distinction as a teacher and lecturer.[14]

These are but notes on the life of the Medical Department during its first decade, a period ended by the suspension of its activities following the 1834 Commencement, as Busey wrote, "from some cause." What that cause was we can only speculate.

CHAPTER FOUR

The Reorganized Medical Department

For five years, no mention of the Medical Department was made in the *Minutes* of the Board of Trustees of the College. Then, on July 29, 1839, "Dr. Sewall presented to the Board, a communication stating that the time has now arrived which was believed peculiarly favorable to the restoration of the medical school and the establishment on a basis calculated to render a permanent and useful institution." The last election of members of the faculty for the usual three-year term had been held on April 27, 1836. The Board's assent to Dr. Sewall's proposal took the form of an election of the faculty. Quite regardless of anything else, it was the normal time to take such action. The following were elected: Dr. Sewall, Professor of Pathology and the Practice of Medicine; Dr. Jones, Professor of Chemistry and Pharmacy; Dr. Lindsly, Professor of Obstetrics and the Diseases of Women and Children; Dr. Miller, Professor of Surgery; Dr. Thomas, Professor of Materia Medica, Therapeutics and Hygiene; Dr. May, Professor of Anatomy and Physiology.

Dr. Thomas Sewall and Dr. Thomas P. Jones have been mentioned before. Dr. Harvey Lindsly (1804-1889), A.M. 1820 Princeton, and M.D. 1828 Columbian, Professor of Obstetrics, 1839-1845, and of Pathology and the Practice of Medicine, 1845-1846, had a long and distinguished career as practitioner, teacher, and leader in professional organizations. He was president of the Board of Health of Washington, 1836-1846, an incorporator of the renewed Medical Society of the District, and a founder of the Medical Association of the District and of the Washington Infirmary. He was president of the American Medical Association in 1859. For over thirty years Dr. Lindsly was chairman of the executive committee of the American Colonization Society which founded Liberia. An insistence, at times, on the formal recognition of his seniority in faculty rank was perhaps understandable in the light of his many achievements.[1] Dr. Busey describes him as "a noted example of that small class of medical men who can confine themselves to their own business, and avoid all alliances and complications which disturb the equanimity and peace of one's own life." It was just this quality which, in a period of great stress, brought to him the high honor of election to the presidency of the American Medical Association.[2]

Dr. Thomas Miller (1806-1873), Professor of Surgery, 1839-1840, and Professor of Anatomy, 1840-1859, was a native of Virginia and a graduate of the University of Pennsylvania. Engaged in teaching privately for a few years after his graduation, he quickly became active in the work of professional organization. He was president of the Board of Health for nine years, and a member of the Board of Aldermen. His considerable influence was used in furthering many constructive projects, among them the establishment of the government hospital and the movement to enforce a system for the registration of births and deaths. Dr. Miller, along with Dr. Lindsly and Dr. John M. Thomas, was appointed by President Tyler a physician in charge of the hospital, which, when completed, became the Washington Infirmary. When he was made professor emeritus in 1859, he was hailed as "the Nestor of the Profession in the District."[3] He was a man with a strong sense of civic obligation, of professional responsibility, and personal duty, and a great espouser of causes which he pursued with vigor and courage.[4]

Dr. John Moylan Thomas (1805-1853), a graduate of the University of Maryland, was professor of materia medica, therapeutics and hygiene, 1839-1844, and of physiology, 1844-1848. He was a member of the Board of Examiners, 1840-1849. Dr. Busey's appraisal of him varies from what would seem to be his general rule of "de mortuis nil nisi bonum." It had better be quoted than paraphrased:

John M. Thomas came leisurely after time to his lectures on physiology, which were brief, polished, and unsatisfactory. He was always dressed in the latest style, dignified, polite, but very reserved. At that time he had a very large business among the better class of citizens and lived sumptuously. Some years later, I parted with him in front of John Foy's saloon about one hour before he wrote the prescription which, it was alleged, killed a porter at Fuller's Hotel, and the last time I saw him he was struggling, with assistance, to enter a carriage to respond to a summons to see Mrs. Adams.

This is indeed a vivid memory of an old professor after fifty years.[5]

Dr. John Frederick May (1812-1891), A.B. 1831, M.D. 1834, who served as professor of anatomy, 1839-1840, of physiology, 1839-1842, and of surgery, 1840-1842, 1845-1858, was the son of Dr. Frederick May (1773-1847), Professor of Obstetrics in the first Medical faculty. After his graduation Dr. John Frederick May spent over a year in the hospitals of London and Paris. Part of his professional career was spent in Nashville and in New York. Through his skill as a surgeon he touched history at two tragic moments. He is said to have been called to the bedside of President Lincoln in the little house on 10th Street, where, after probing the wound, he confirmed the opinion that nothing could be done to save the President's life. Somewhat later, he was summoned to the Navy Yard to view a body which he identified as that of the assassin Booth, through a scar which had resulted from the removal of a tumor on the back of the neck by Dr. May.[6]

Of the hundreds of his medical forerunners and contemporaries upon whom Busey passes judgment, none receives higher praise than John Frederick May. Busey refers to him in a lengthy eulogy as "a very distinguished physician, both as a surgeon and a general practitioner," who "was perhaps, the first resident physician whose reputation extended beyond the 'Ten Miles Square' and brought to him important cases for treatment."[7]

These were the rather exceptional men elected to the Medical faculty when its lectures were resumed. *The Globe* announced the beginning of the course in medicine on Monday, November 4, 1839, in the Medical College, 10th and E Streets, at twelve o'clock each day during the week according to the following order:[8]

Monday	Dr. May
Tuesday	Dr. Thomas
Wednesday	Dr. Miller
Thursday	Dr. Lindsly
Friday	Dr. Jones
Saturday	Dr. Sewall

The announcement of the beginning of the course in 1839 is similar to kindred announcements that had appeared in the years before 1834. There is no mention of a resumption of lectures. It would appear that there had been no interruption. Consequently there is no reference to causes of the interruption or of the resumption. This silence rather stimulates speculation in the light of the minutes of the first meeting recorded in what is labeled as *Dean's Book, Medical Department, Columbian College*. The inside title is more descriptive: "Minutes of the Meetings of the Medical Professors of the Columbian College."

The first entry was dated "Wednesday June 1839," the day of the month being omitted. The entry was signed by "J. Frederick May Sec." It stated that at the request of Dr. Thomas Sewall, Professor of Anatomy and Physiology, there had met at his office: Dr. Thomas Sewall, Dr. Thomas P. Jones, Dr. Harvey Lindsly, Dr. Thomas Miller, Dr. J. M. Thomas, Dr. J. F. May, Dr. J. C. Hall, Professor of Surgery, and Dr. Frederick May, Professor of Obstetrics. The purpose of the meeting was to consider "the practicability of attempting to reorganize the Medical Department of the Columbian College. Whereupon, it was determined to make the effort." To proceed to this end it was deemed desirable that those holding chairs—Drs. Sewall, Hall, and Frederick May—formally declare their willingness to cooperate. Dr. Sewall agreed, but Drs. Hall and May declined and presented their resignations to the Board of Trustees. Proceeding then to nominate for approval by the Trustees holders of the various chairs, the following were named:

> Thomas Sewall, M.D., Professor of Pathology and the Practice of Medicine
> Thomas P. Jones, M.D., Professor of Chemistry
> Harvey Lindsly, M.D., Professor of Obstetrics and Diseases of Women and Children
> Thomas Miller, M.D., Professor of Principles and Practice of Surgery
> J. M. Thomas, M.D., Professor of Therapeutics and Materia Medica
> J. F. May, M.D., Professor of Anatomy and Physiology

Dr. Sewall, being senior, was designated chairman of the faculty, and Dr. May secretary.

At a second meeting on Saturday, June ?, 1839, the organization of the faculty was continued. Dr. Sewall as chairman was exempted from serving as dean, but his five associates were each to serve for a year in the following order: Drs. May, Thomas, Miller, and Lindsly, and Jones. The treasurer or dean was to keep an account of all moneys received or disbursed, to be presented to the faculty once a year for settlement. It was:

> Resolved that in view of the spirit which has brought about this reorganization of the Medical School, all conversations and observations involving persons

not members of the Faculty be considered as offered under the most solemn sanction of honorable confidence.

The faculty as named at this meeting was approved by the Trustees on July 29, 1839.[9]

With the faculty organized, the next problem was to find a suitable building for the delivery of lectures, to be called "the Medical College." At the July, 1839, meeting of the faculty, it was reported that the Purdy building at the corner of 4½ Street and Louisiana Avenue had been leased for five years at $500 per year, the professors being responsible for all necessary fixtures. The employment of a janitor was authorized, and a circular was ordered prepared for submission to the faculty for adoption. The meeting resolved "that each professor shall bear an equal proportion of the expenses of the school."

In a month's time the circular was ready. It announced that a large and commodious building on the corner of 4½ Street and Louisiana Avenue had been acquired and that in it were "particular arrangements for the study of practical anatomy." Senators and delegates were each given the right to nominate for one scholarship. The total expense for the full course by all professors was $70; a dissecting ticket at $10 was optional. To graduate, a student must attend the lectures of each professor for two full courses, or one course there and another "in a respectable institution." Names were to be filed with the dean for graduation, and an inaugural dissertation on some medical subject was to be presented to him at least thirty days before the close of the session. Upon passing a satisfactory examination the candidate would be recommended for the degree of Doctor of Medicine. Good board could be obtained at from three to four dollars per week. The circular as presented was dated August 12, 1839. It was to have to undergo a very significant correction.

On August 16, it was reported to the faculty that the old Medical College, located on the northeast corner of 10th and E Streets, which the faculty had occupied until the suspension of lectures in 1834, was available. These quarters were in every way preferable to the Purdy building. The property had passed out of the faculty's control and was now owned by General J. P. Van Ness, a former Trustee of the College. The faculty was fortunately able to get out of its dilemma. John Purdy agreed to cancel the five-year lease upon payment of $100. General Van Ness asked $600 a year for the 10th and E Street location, as against John Purdy's contracted annual charge of $500; but to indemnify the faculty in part for the $100 they had to pay Purdy for his release, General Van Ness agreed to reduce the rent to $550 for the first year and, in addition, to have all repairs and fixtures made ready for opening on the first Monday in November. The Medical Department resumed its residence at the old address.

During the five years that the faculty was General Van Ness' tenant, the dean announced each quarter an assessment of $25 on each member to pay the rent. The last assessment for the payment of rent was announced on October 21, 1844.

Faculty approval of the arrangement for the change in buildings was unanimous but for the objection of the professor of chemistry, who claimed that "[for reasons given] his loss would be great." Professor Jones, as stated above, was a highly popular lecturer on chemistry and it was in this connection that his alleged loss would occur. A special arrangement was made in his case. He was relieved from his share of the expenses of the building (the $25 quarterly assessment) except for incidental expenses and was permitted to sell tickets for the lectures to citizens. In return he agreed to pay to the faculty money received from tickets sold to other than students unless that amount was greater than that received from each of the other professors. Simply put, he was to be allowed to earn his share of the expenses by his lecture fees from the public. Otherwise, everyone was pleased and delighted with General Van Ness' agreement "to replace the building in the same state and rendered as safe and secure as it was when occupied as a medical college."[10]

In the light of the efforts expended to bring the building back to its original condition, a fire that began in an adjoining building and spread to the Medical College was particularly unfortunate. At a special meeting of the faculty in April, 1840, it was reported that the damage had been considerable, "that there had been many unpleasant developments of anatomical specimens," and that men had been employed to clean up the building and the yard. The dean was instructed to pay necessary charges, not covered by the owner's policy, out of the general fund and to request General Van Ness to have the building repaired as speedily as possible.

On July 6, 1840, Professor Thomas P. Jones offered his resignation as professor of chemistry because his "other avocations required during the winter the entire direction of my time to their performance." At its next meeting the faculty nominated Dr. Frederick Hall as Professor Jones' successor. Difficulties developed with Professor Jones when a survey was undertaken to see that proper apparatus was on hand for the use of the incoming professor. Jones said that the apparatus he had used was, for the most part, his own property; that what was originally provided had time after time been replaced at his own expense; and that what remained in use was part of the philosophical equipment of the College. Refusing to turn over what he had, he was asked to state what had been taken from the laboratory of the College, what returned, and what he retained. Jones said he could not give the information, that what had been broken or spoiled was of less value than what he had had to buy. A second demand from the dean brought forth a list of sorts, with a tart rejoinder to the faculty against the tone of the resolutions passed in his case. The dean was instructed to get from Dr. Jones the articles named in his letter. Professor Hall, Jones' successor, stated that about $600 would have to be spent on equipment, whereupon a special assessment of $50 was levied upon each member. The building was in complete repair and fully equipped in time for the opening of the new session.[11]

While no cause was specifically stated for the period of suspension which was then ending, an inkling was given by the meticulous care and detail with which financial and personnel matters were spelled out. In all of this Dr. Sewall, referred to at times as the chairman and at least once as the president of the faculty, took the initiative. Whatever had happened before, he was not going to repeat past errors.

On September 28, 1839, he offered and secured acceptance for a code of ethics under the title "Private Articles of Agreement." The preamble is significant. It sounds almost like a Scots' verdict on something that had gone before:

Aware of the importance of mutual confidence and entire harmony among our faculty, whose object in uniting their labors is to rear up a great and useful Medical School at the seat of the National Government; and aware also of the liability there is to collision and discord among the most respected and upright men, from mistakes, misapprehensions as well as misrepresentations of others, and aware that the success of our school is to depend not upon the labor or character of any one of the faculty, but upon the character and labours of each and the harmony of all.

Therefore the undersigned professors of the Medical Department of the Columbian College, do pledge ourselves to each other:

    To exercise a spirit of courtesy, kindness and forbearance;

    To endeavor to secure for each other respect of the medical class;

    To pass on any information useful to the School or to themselves as individuals;

To show deference and respect to each in his appropriate branch in which he is to be regarded as an authority;

To attempt a settlement in the event of misunderstanding and prejudice between two or more members of the faculty, and if he fail report to the Board of Trustees "whose decision shall be final and satisfactory," these provisions to apply to both professional and private interests and character.

To these Private Articles of Agreement, the faculty added in November, 1842, preceded by a preamble similar in tone to the one quoted above, an agreement on the part of each member not to interfere or in any way "to insinuate himself into the favour of any individual or family with a view of becoming their physician, when such family or individual has already selected their medical attendant."

Going on then to a discussion of standing regulations in regard to the organization of the School, the faculty adopted such of the regulations of 1824 governing the original establishment as were applicable to the reorganized School. Under the caption "On Lectures," the six branches were listed and provisions for time and length of term stipulated. Under the rubric "Of Students," fees were stated; medical students were declared subject to the rules of discipline established by the Board and administered by the faculty, and were allowed to take courses in the College without charge.

In the section "Of Degrees," the requirements for graduation were spelled out in full:

1. The fee for examination was $20 and for the diploma $5, to be paid in advance by each candidate;
2. Theses would be examined and examinations would be held in the order of presentation of theses to the dean;
3. The dean might return a thesis on account of carelessness in writing, false syntax, or faults in orthography;
4. The dean should give a student twenty-four hours' notice of his examination;
5. The thesis must be written on letter paper and be considered the property of the College;
6. All charges must be paid before examination; if failed, fees would be returned;
7. Examinations were to begin on the Monday following the close

Minutes

*Of the Meetings of the Medical Professors
of the*

Columbian College.

Wednesday, June. 1839.

At the request of Thomas Sewall M.D professor
of Anatomy & Physiology in Medical Department of the
Columbian College. the following Medical Gentlemen
met at his office at 12 oclock. M. vz. Thomas Sewall M.D.
Thomas P Jones M.D. Harvey Lindsly M.D. Thomas Miller M.D
J W Thomas M.D. J Fredk. May M.D. J. C. Hall M.D professor
of Pan. & prac. Surgery & Fredk. May M.D Prof obstet & diseases
of Women & children.

The object of the meeting. was stated to be. to take into con
-sideration the practicability of attempting to reorganize the
Medical Department of the Columbian College. Whereupon
it was determined to make the effort. It was necessary to ascertain
whether. the Professor of Obstet & diseases of women & children. and Dr
F May. and the Professor of Anatomy & Physiology. Dr T Sewall
And the Professor of Surgery Dr J C Hall could unite in the
object or resign their chairs— Upon the object of the meeting
being stated to them and a desire that they should cooperate to Dr. May
& May. & J C Hall declined & presented their resignation, as one
to the board of Trustees— Dr Sewall agreed to cooperate in the
reorganization of the school. and the following gentlemen were nominated
to fill the vacant chairs vz.

Thomas Sewall M.D. for Prof of Pathology & Prax Medicine.
Thomas P Jones M.D " " Chemistry
Harvey Lindsly M.D " " Obstet & diseases of women & children
Thomas Miller M.D " " Chirurg. Princl. & Prax
J W Thomas M.D " " Therapeutics & Mat Meds
Jno Fred May M.D " " Anat & Physiology

The Dean's Book, Vol. I, p. 1. The first page of The Dean's Book, recording
the reorganization of the Medical Department in 1839.

The Washington Infirmary. The use of this structure in Judiciary Square, originally the jail but reconstructed as an insane asylum, was granted to the Medical faculty by Congressional action on June 15, 1844, "for purposes of an infirmary, for medical instruction, and scientific purposes." In this form (*above*), it was used until 1852, when, on petition of the Medical faculty, Congress appropriated $20,000 "to enlarge the accommodations for the benefit of the sick and the treatment of paupers" (*below*).

Destruction of the Infirmary, 1861. Requisitioned by the government for use as a military hospital at the outbreak of the War of 1861-1865, the Infirmary was totally destroyed by a fire which broke out at 1 A.M. on November 4, 1861.

Sisters of Charity. During the greater part of its history, nursing care in the Infirmary was given by the Sisters of Charity. The habit worn by the Sisters during the earlier part of their service is shown in the portrait of Mother Seton, foundress of the Sisters of Charity in the United States *(left)*. Just before the destruction of the building and after the American Sisters of Charity had joined the original foundation of St. Vincent de Paul in Paris, the more familiar habit was worn as shown *(right)* in the portrait of Mother Mathilde Inchelin, Superioress General of the world-wide Daughters of Charity.

Thomas Miller, M.D., President of the faculty, 1845-1855, 1860-1873; Professor of Surgery, 1839-1840, of Anatomy, 1840-1859, of Physiology, 1842-1844, 1854-1859, Emeritus, 1859-1873.

Harvey Lindsly, M.D., Professor of Obstetrics, 1839-1845, of Pathology and of the Practice of Medicine, 1845-1846; President of the American Medical Association.

Joshua Riley, M.D., President of the faculty, 1856-1857; Professor of Materia Medica, 1844-1859, of Hygiene, 1850-1859.

John C. Riley, M.D., Professor of Materia Medica, 1859-1879; Dean of the Faculty, 1859-1879.

Alexander Yelverton Peyton Garnett, M.D.,
Professor of Anatomy, 1854-1855, of Clinical Medicine, 1858-1861, 1866-1888; President of the Faculty, 1876-1887.

Robert King Stone, M.D., Professor of
Anatomy and Physiology, 1848-1854, of
Ophthalmological Anatomy, 1858-1859;
Personal Physician of President Lincoln.

Frederick May, M.D., Professor of Obstetrics, 1825-1839.

John Frederick May, M.D., Professor of
Anatomy and Physiology, 1831-1842, of
Surgery, 1845-1858.

Tenth Street, about the turn of the century, showing Ford's Theatre and, at the northeast corner of Tenth and E Streets, the first Medical School. The peculiar shape of the roof was due to an effort to secure as much daylight as possible for the anatomical department on the top floor. (Washingtoniana Collection, D.C. Public Library.)

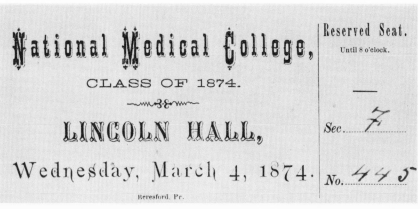

In the Days of Lavish Commencements. A characteristic announcement of Commencement and a ticket of admission for the exercises in Lincoln Hall on March 4, 1874.

The Medical Center Area during the War of 1861-1865. An infantry regiment in formation on 23rd Street, south of Washington Circle.

of the course, or any other day designated by the faculty, beginning at 11 A.M. or any other hour set;

8. Examinations were to be private and all matters concerning them considered confidential;

9. As soon as theses were received the dean should call a meeting and distribute them among the faculty;

10. The examination was to cover all branches;

11. If any professor was absent from an examination, his colleagues would conduct the examination;

12. When the examination of each candidate was completed, the dean would count the ballots, with two negative votes sufficient to reject the candidate;

13. The dean should advise the candidate if rejected, and return fees;

14. If the candidate passed, the dean should "introduce to the room" and inform him of the faculty's approval;

15. Within twenty-four hours the dean should inform the president of the College and the president of the Board with a certified list of those passed and request the Board's mandamus.

The section "Of the Commencement" fixed the order of the exercises and required the dean to deliver the charge.

The faculty directed that the dean read the parts of the ordinance referring to candidates for degrees at least once in every two weeks during the course. Repetition as a pedagogical device was held in high esteem—or was this merely an overdose of due notice?[12]

It would appear that meetings of the faculty were conducted with great decorum. The *Minutes* refer to members of the faculty by title, rather than by name. Under the ordinance stated meetings were held on the first Monday in January, April, July, and October. Special meetings could be held at the dean's call when requested by two professors. The limited size of the group did in a sense temper the formality of the meetings. The *Minutes* invariably use the phrase "after conversation" rather than "after discussion," and the resolutions are set forth in a positive fashion as though they were "the sense of the meeting" rather than the result of a split vote, amendment, or compromise.

It must not be assumed, however, that recommendation for the degree was automatic. A glimpse of the outcome of the examination in 1844 is illuminating. There were two steps in the final stage of a student's career, one involving the acceptance of his thesis as a required preliminary to final examinations and the other the final examination. In February, 1844, one student "was censured for bad spelling and recommended to give attention to orthography." The dean advised him "to study faithfully his profession." The thesis of another student was returned to him with the information "that it precluded the possibility of being examined." It was written on yellow paper. The spelling was such that the faculty could not accept it. On the first page there were no less than eighteen errors in spelling and the violation of the simplest rules of grammar. The handwriting was also very bad. A candidate who had come up for the examination before and had failed but who was permitted to come up again, received on his second attempt one vote for and four against. His request for a third trial was denied. Another student who failed and asked for an immediate reexamination was told that if he studied, he could come up for reexamination in June, three months later. Of the eleven candidates in 1844, one passed very well, four passed well, three passed, two were rejected, and one thesis was not accepted.

The examination of candidates was held in strict conformity with what had apparently become a customary ritual and the form in which it was reported never varied. That form was as follows:

The Dean introduced Mr. X from [state]. Having complied with the regulations of the institution, Mr. X was admitted to examination. His thesis on —— has been examined and approved by Professor —— and he having passed to the perfect satisfaction of the faculty, it was resolved to recommend Mr. X to the Trustees for the degree of Doctor of Medicine.[13]

It had been a standing custom to permit each Senator and delegate to name a beneficiary and mention of this had been regularly made in the circulars. Difficulties in administration arose. A young man writing from the U.S. Hospital, Headquarters Marine Corps, on October 16, 1841, stated that he had been certified as a proper person to attend the lectures without charge by the secretary of state of New Jersey. His claim was questioned because he was then resident in Washington. He stated that he was on a visit to Washington when he was offered the job at the hospital by his preceptor, Dr. John A. Kearney, Surgeon, U.S.N., whose degree was an honorary one granted in 1840 by Columbian. On the basis of the explanation the student was admitted as a beneficiary. A month later when a resident of New York applied on the basis of a recommendation of a Senator from Missouri, it was agreed that a Senator could adopt a student of another state, provided that his state was not already supplied among the beneficiaries.[14] In the following year two students were permitted to attend lectures without certificates until Congress convened and the Senators would be in the city to furnish the required endorsements.[15]

Because it was felt that the beneficiary system had been abused, it was wholly repealed on March 10, 1843. Hereafter impecunious young men who wanted to begin the study of medicine were told to give notes satisfactorily endorsed.[16]

When a young man training for missionary service had difficulties because of his limited means and asked to be given leave to attend gratuitously as a beneficiary from his state, action on his request was postponed for two weeks. Then he was informed that his request would be granted if he would give his notes for the amount due and go out as a missionary with the understanding that the faculty would not insist on his payment of the notes. The regulations were upheld, but with an escape clause.[17]

The days of loose financial administration were over. No professor was permitted to give his ticket to a student without first receiving the fee or a note endorsed by "a respectable resident of this city." Unless such an arrangement was made within three weeks after the beginning of the session, full credit for that session would not be given.[18] In a period when a successful medical man was said to have not "a large practice" but "a large business," it is surprising that it took so long to establish sound business practices in medical education.[19]

In the five years 1839-1844 under consideration here, the record shows little communication between faculty and student body. There appear some resolutions of appreciation from time to time, and one of criticism of the irregularity of lecturers. Petitions were regularly presented asking that Christmas and New Year's Day and, at times, the day preceding or following, be granted as holidays. In a few cases, a shortening of the term was requested. The students' petitions were regularly granted.

The five years 1839-1844 fall within what a recent writer has described "as for the most part dull decades of educational stagnation and trade school competition." Certainly the first of these observations applied to the Medical Department of Columbian College. Educational organization retained the lines laid down in the 1824 ordinances. There were a shuffling of the chairs and a changing of class schedules from time to time, with little apparent effect. The purchase of dissecting tickets, at first optional, became obligatory. A committee to consider reorganization of the

School and the propriety of having a professorship of the institutes of medicine was appointed in 1844.[20]

Special lectures or series of lectures were held in the College from time to time, generally in the summer and spring when the rooms were not in demand for regular instruction. Interestingly enough, the circular of 1843 announced an annual summer session beginning on the first Monday in May and continuing for four months. A special staff of seven lecturers covered the standard branches of the subject.

The faculty normally consisted of six professors, with a demonstrator or prosector of anatomy. A characteristic teaching schedule was the one given for the 1844-1845 course beginning November 5, at 10 A.M.[21]

Programme

	10 A.M. to 11 A.M.	*11 to 12*	*12 to 1*	*1 to 2*
Monday	Prof. Johnston Clinical lect.	Prof. Thomas	Prof. Sewall	Prof. Miller
Tuesday	Prof. Johnston Surgical lect.	Prof. Thomas	Prof. Sewall	Prof. Miller
Wednesday	Prof. Miller Clinical lect.	Prof. Thomas	Prof. Sewall	Prof. Miller
Thursday	Prof. Johnston Surgical lect.	Prof. Lindsly	Prof. Sewall	Prof. Miller
Friday	Prof. Sewall Clinical lect.	Prof. Thomas	Prof. Sewall	Prof. Miller
Saturday	Prof. Johnston Surgical lect.	Prof. Lindsly	Prof. Sewall	Prof. Miller

Professor Page on Tuesday, Thursday, and Saturday at 5 P.M.

The requirement that two full courses of lectures (or at least one by a transfer student) must be taken might occasion some surprise, inasmuch as only one course was given, and the entire field was covered in that course. The same course was taken twice. Why? Designed at first to meet a practical difficulty, this arrangement by 1820 had become common usage. It had been done originally by the late eighteenth-century schools to meet the problem raised by a shortage of textbooks, teaching materials, and instructors. By offering a single course instead of two graded courses, it was felt that, aside from economy, the student gained a clearer and fuller knowledge of his subject. Because it was done in the schools of great prestige in Philadelphia and New York, it was looked upon as the normal arrangement.[22]

The faculty had in mind both public service and the improvement of teaching when on June 23, 1843, it was decided to mature as soon as possible a plan for the organization of a Public Dispensary under the immediate control of the faculty, with clinical lectures to be given on the patients who applied for medical advice. The plan was put into operation the following session, with consultation at the Dispensary daily except Sunday, between 10 and 11 A.M. Assignment of physicians was made for a month at a time. For the first month, these were assigned as follows:

Dr. Sewall, assisted by Dr. Howard, Monday and Thursday
Dr. Johnston, assisted by Dr. Eliot, Tuesday and Friday
Dr. Thomas, assisted by Dr. Smoot, Wednesday and Saturday

Handbills relating to the Dispensary were printed and distributed about the city. The records show a bill of $33.11¼ paid for medicine furnished the Dispensary for the session.[23]

To publicize the courses, five or six hundred copies of the circular were printed each year and put in the hands of physicians and other interested persons. In addition, notices were placed in newspapers and periodicals. The advertising schedule for 1841 called for publication of the announcement for the winter term as follows: once a month from June to May in the *Philadelphia Medical Examiner* and the *Boston Medical and Surgical Journal;* four times a month from the first of August in the *New York Observer;* once a week from the first of August in the *Richmond Inquirer,* the *Louisville Journal, The Globe* of Washington, and the *Charleston Mercury;* and once a week from the first of May in the *National Intelligencer* of Washington.[24]

During the years 1839-1844, financing was relatively simple and completely in the hands of the faculty, with only the graduation fee being turned over to the College. Tickets for each professor's lecture costing $10 or $15 each were sold by the professor and the fees retained by him. The matriculation fee and the examination fee made up "the funds of the School" and were received by the dean and used to pay incidental expenses and administrative costs. At the end of each year the balance was divided among the members of the faculty. The amount of this balance was not usually stated; for the 1842-1843 session it was $126.45. Rent was taken care of separately. During this period, each member of the faculty was assessed $25 quarterly. The average net compensation for a professor's lectures over a four-month period probably did not exceed $300. During the preceptorial year when a student was studying under a single practitioner prior to taking the prescribed courses of lectures, a substantial fee was paid to the preceptor.[25]

The preceding pages, drawn from the faculty records of the Medical Department of the Columbian College, give a picture of the typical proprietary medical school of the past century. The reorganized School of 1839-1840 profited by the experience of the decade and a half which had preceded it, with nine sizable classes in as many years and then five years without any in a period of suspension. The meticulous care with which rules were drawn up and enforced and the careful administration of its finances show a determination to make the system work. The influence of Thomas Sewall is evident everywhere. He was the driving force, the legislator who determined the character of the School and led it into a new period, where different conditions were to prevail.

The five-year lease on the building ran until November 1, 1844. In anticipation of its expiration, a committee visited General Van Ness eleven months before to inquire if he would make necessary repairs on the building, and if not, for what sum a new lot could be acquired and a building erected according to plans furnished by them. General Van Ness agreed that if the lease were renewed for five years, he would expend $500 for repairs, the rent to be $500 per annum for the first and second years and $600 per annum for the remaining three years. The faculty made some slight revisions in the terms and agreed, if the general assented, to renew the lease.

Dr. Sewall, however, had been active along other lines. On May 23, 1844, he told the faculty that it was his opinion and that of others that the building recently conditioned for an insane hospital might be obtained from the President or by a joint resolution of the Congress in place of the building then occupied. Events moved rapidly. On June 15, 1844, Congress passed "An Act making appropriation for the support of insane persons in the District of Columbia, and for other purposes." Section 2 of that act reads:

And be it further enacted, that the Commissioner of Public Works is directed to allow the Medical Faculty of the Columbian College in the District of Columbia, to occupy the insane hospital, with the adjoining grounds, situated in the Judiciary Square in Washington, for purposes of an infirmary, for medical instruction, and for scientific purposes, on condition that they shall give satisfactory security to keep the said building in repairs, and return it, with the grounds to the Government, in as good condition as they are now in, whenever required to do so.

Five days after the approval of the act the members of the faculty formally bound themselves and their successors to the United States in the sum of $10,000 if they failed to fulfill the conditions cited in the act. Major Noland, the Commissioner of Public Works, then escorted the dean to the insane asylum and formally transferred the building to him.

There were but three months and a half before the new session was to begin, and haste had to be made. Three times during the summer special assessments of $50 were made on the members of the faculty to defray costs of alteration. A man by the name of Clokey was appointed steward to superintend the Infirmary. He was assigned a two-story building in the rear as a residence for himself and family. The steward was to furnish, as needed, beds, bedding, and other necessary furniture, a sufficient number of competent nurses, and the diet prescribed for the sick. A reasonable compensation was to be agreed upon.

Housing in a public building entailed certain obligations, and members of the City Council pressed for information as to the terms upon which the Infirmary would receive such of the poor as they were called upon to care for. After consultation it was agreed that an effort would be made to have a bill passed for their support and medical attention in the Infirmary.

Confident that all arrangements could be made, the faculty gave formal notice through the public prints of the early opening of the Infirmary. With a teaching hospital under the faculty's charge, a new era in medical education was about to begin.[26]

The "Medical College," as it was called, at 10th and E Streets had been the faculty's first permanent home. They had occupied it for nine years as owners and for five years as tenants. From 1868 to 1886 it was occupied by the Medical School of Georgetown University.[27]

In a sense, the old Medical College was the cradle of medical education in the District of Columbia.

CHAPTER FIVE

The Washington Infirmary

The removal of the Medical Department from 10th and E Streets to Judiciary Square did not decrease the problems of the faculty. It increased them in a new location. It was only by fortuitous circumstance that this facility was placed at their disposal. Public pressure on Congress for the establishment of a public hospital had been constant. For five years, from 1832 to 1837, a committee of the Board of Health actively urged Congress to appropriate funds for such an institution. When the inmates of the old jail were removed to a new building, Congress passed a law authorizing the old jail on Judiciary Square to be refitted for an insane asylum at a cost of $10,000. But when the remodeling was completed, it was decided that the location was improper for an insane asylum. It was at this time that, by law, Congress allowed the Medical faculty to occupy the building for "an infirmary, for medical instruction and scientific purposes." While the building was given rent-free, the major expense for equipping and adapting the building to their purposes rested solely on the faculty. Dr. Toner's praise in his *Anniversary Oration* is well merited: "These gentlemen deserve the lasting gratitude of this community, and the highest respect and admiration of their professional brethren, for the tact, energy, and enterprise displayed in establishing the Washington Infirmary."[1]

The building described as "situated immediately in the rear [i.e., the north] of the City Hall [at the head of 4½ Street]," was two stories high, with a frontage of about 150 feet. Patients, it was announced, would be received upon paying a very small sum to the steward for board, with medical attention furnished gratuitously. The poor who appeared daily between 9 and 10 A.M. would receive advice and medicines without charge. Student fees for a complete course amounted to $90, with a demonstrator's ticket costing $10 additional. Clinical lectures were given and operations performed on patients from the Infirmary and the Public Dispensary.[2]

Up to this time, the guiding hand in shaping the destinies of the Medical Department had been that of Dr. Thomas Sewall, its senior professor. Just when new problems were arising and when his sound judgment, his deep learning, and his influence would have been most useful, Dr. Sewall died of tuberculosis. When his death was announced to the faculty on April 10, 1845, it was immediately resolved that a badge of mourning should be worn for thirty days. An eloquent and touching eulogy by Professor Thomas was concluded with these words:

Here, in this institution of which he was the sage counsellor, the able advocate, the bright ornament, a train of grateful emotions will long combine his name with the mention of this place; and the ardent student, while he aspires to emulate his virtue and his success, will indulge his enthusiasm by inspecting the institution which he advanced and the halls where he lectured.

To this warm personal eulogy by a friend and colleague we can add the judicious appraisal made a century later by the biographers of Dr. Henry Sewall, his grandson and a distinguished physiologist and physician, who referred to Dr. Thomas Sewall as "a prominent physician in the early days of the republic, who was noted as an experimental scientist, as a professor of medicine, and as a writer on medical subjects."[3]

On September 6, 1845, Dr. Thomas Miller was elected chairman of the faculty to succeed the late Dr. Sewall. The extent of the powers and functions of the chairman is not always clear. That Dr. Sewall should have been considered first among his peers was to be expected on the basis of seniority alone, if for no other reason. In the *Minutes*, when not referred to by name or chair, he was called "Chairman" but rarely "President." The office of chairman was an elective one, in theory at least, subject to annual election with no limit on reelection. The chairman's name was the first stated in the list of those present at a meeting. The chairman was excused from serving as dean, an office held in rotation by the other members of the faculty for a normal term of one year. The dean kept the *Minutes* of the faculty, dealt with students, received and disbursed most of the funds, and discharged other assigned functions. Much of the work of the faculty was done by small committees of two or three. In this way practically all were involved in the general work of a common venture. They were to have plenty to do.

The Congress had been generous, but along with the responsibilities entailed, its generosity had been limited to a bare building, remodeled for a different use, but adaptable for the purposes of the Medical faculty. Problems were three in number: financial, personnel, and professional jealousy.

Finances became exceedingly involved. There were still unpaid bills to be taken care of, necessitating special assessments of $50 and $25. A special committee was appointed to decide on what would have to be done to make the building usable by way of furniture, means of heating and ventilating, baths and other facilities, all involving heavy outlays. A subscription list was prepared for raising a hospital fund, and the city corporation and the Secretary of the Treasury were petitioned to send to the new hospital the sick over whom they had control. Complying with the request, the Secretary of the Treasury directed the collectors of the ports of Alexandria and Georgetown to send all sick and disabled seamen, entitled to the benefits of the hospital fund, to the Hospital for a period not to exceed four months at a cost of $3 a week. No one suffering from an incurable disease was to be admitted, and the cost of transportation from Alexandria was to be borne by the Hospital.

A board of visitors, with the mayor as chairman and representatives of each ward as members, was set up to make quarterly inspections and to give an annual report in the hope that an informed public would contribute to the relief of poor patients. Although the board included such eminent citizens as Peter Force and Colonel Archibald Henderson, it failed to bring in funds. To give time for the accumulation of some resources, patients were not generally admitted until September 1, 1845, and the wards remained closed. The arrangement of the Dispensary got under way August 29, 1845.

Mention should be made of an evidence of institutional solidarity that occurred at this time. In spite of their own financial problems, the dean was directed by the faculty to give their note for $200 as a contribution to the College's professorship fund.

Preparatory to a general admission of patients, the charge for board in the Hospital was fixed at $4 per week, for mariners $3, for patients with delirium tremens $5 to $10. Patients were to pay in advance, or make special arrangements, and to reimburse the Hospital for all breakage. No charity patient would be received. All patients with smallpox were to be sent to a special building provided for that purpose by the district authorities.

In March, 1845, Drs. Miller and Johnston were appointed physicians and Drs. Riley and Lindsly surgeons to the Hospital. Announced along with these appointments was the notice "that Professor Page would apply the magnetic-electric and galvanic influence to such patients who desired to test the efficacy of such means in the treatment of their diseases." Mrs. Adamson, the wife of the janitor, was appointed for the time to attend patients and furnish them with their diet, for which she was to be paid $2 per week per patient. This arrangement was but a stopgap and there was discussion as to whether two Sisters of Charity should be engaged as nurses, or a steward employed.

Negotiations with the Sisters of Charity went on through the early summer of 1846. The Sisters were straightforward and positive in their requirements. The dean was to be answerable for their protection and support; expenses of each Sister for clothing amounting to $50 per year and for traveling or expenses due to illness were to be paid to the Sister Supervisor every six months. Sisters who became ill would be supported by the Infirmary. They would point out the number of attendants, male or female, that would be required for "the drudgery of the house"; their chief attention would be devoted to the welfare of the patients. The Sisters would preside over the internal arrangements of the house without interference. The dean would make all of the "heaviest" purchases for the house, while the Sisters would make smaller or extra ones with funds in advance, for which an accounting would be given. Patients would be admitted by the Sister Supervisor on order from the dean or, in his absence, from any of the administrators. The physician would make his daily visit at an hour that would suit the Sisters, but they would receive him as early as he required.

The faculty, in general, approved the Sisters' demands but sought some qualifications. By way of clarification it was pointed out that the faculty had sole control of the Hospital. The board of visitors, about which the Sisters were dubious, had had no authority, had been ineffective, should be considered abandoned, and would be formally annulled if the Sisters came. Since the Hospital was a private enterprise, had averaged only between 6 and 12 patients a day, and had not paid its way, they hoped that two Sisters and one female servant would be accepted as adequate, with an agreement to increase the number when the Hospital was more fully patronized. The faculty desired the Sisters to collect board from the patients. The Sisters' reply was positive: at least three Sisters and a male and a female attendant, entire direction and management of internal arrangements of the house without the interference of the faculty, and an immediate reply. The faculty approved the Sisters' demand "if by internal arrangement is meant domestic affairs alone and nothing that relates to the medical or dietetic treatment of patients." On August 3, 1846, it was reported to the faculty that the Sisters had entered upon the performance of their regular duties.[4]

The coming of the Sisters was accompanied by an improvement in the financial situation. Three months after their arrival it was reported that, by the exercise of strict economy, the house would "support itself" from its receipts and that they would enable the Sisters to pay for the winter fuel and groceries. An assessment of $100 on each member of the faculty was made to clear up outstanding bills previously incurred. By way of economy, the faculty sought to make the diet less costly and luxurious by approving a fixed ordinary diet, absolute diet, convalescing diet, and full diet. A resolution praising "the kindness, urbanity and ability of the Sisters presiding" seemed absolutely justified by their efficient services.[5]

On the basis of their experience the Sisters reported after a short time that an average census of at least 15 pay patients would be necessary to carry the Hospital. From the beginning the faculty had been distressed that lack of funds prevented giving the full medical services to the poor and indigent that they desired to render and that the public demanded. A particularly eloquent address to the citizens of the District signed by a faculty committee and taking up more than a full column in the *Intelligencer* of May 26, 1845, presented in great fullness the needs of the Hospital for the care of the indigent. The solid reputation that the Hospital had achieved during the first year of its operation had brought increasing numbers to it for treatment. The building could accommodate from 80 to 100 patients at a time, so there was no problem of room. With proper support, it was felt, 500 patients could be taken care of each year.

"There are," the committee declared, "many, very many who are now solely dependent on the benevolent societies of the District when prostrated by disease, and who consequently can be but imperfectly attended in their afflictions; and we have the opportunity of knowing that there are many, many more whom the friendly and cheering assistance of these humane societies does not reach in their squalid abodes of wretchedness and suffering."

Even so eloquent an appeal produced no appreciable results. Finally, in 1848, Congress began to make an annual appropriation for the support of a fixed number of transient and indigent persons. The amount first appropriated was $2,000, to be expended under the direction of the Commissioner of Public Works. The faculty agreed to maintain an average of 12 patients at all times.[6] The Congressional appropriation varied from year to year from $2,000 to $6,000.[7]

Efforts to get Congressional aid were hampered at times by opposition to the way in which the Hospital was administered. These objections were centered around the claim that the purposes of the Hospital had been distorted to facilitate its use by the Medical College and its faculty.[8] The faculty, obviously, was not unaware of the circulation of these allegations. On April 24, 1847, the dean was directed to have published in the *Union* and the *Intelligencer* a resolution of the faculty which read:

> Resolved, that any physician may place a patient in this Infirmary and have the entire management of the case provided all the regulations of the Institution be strictly adhered to. The usual charge for board will be expected and the medicines furnished such patients will be charged at the same rates as when furnished by one of our city apothecaries.

At the time that this action was taken there was no other school of medicine in the District of Columbia. There had been many attacks on the alleged monopolistic policy of the Medical faculty. Its legal basis had been challenged. Efforts had been made to remove the Infirmary from its control and even to have the building assigned for use as a public secondary school. Suggestions galore for the establishment of another medical college had been made. Until the middle of the century, the *status quo* had been maintained.

On October 25, 1849, three physicians, all of them graduates of the Medical Department—Dr. Flodoardo Howard, 1841; Dr. Johnson Eliot, 1842; and Dr. Noble Young, 1828—decided to establish a medical college under the aegis of Georgetown University. Their formal proposal was accepted on condition that the new school would impose no burdens of any kind on the parent institution. It was felt that Columbian's control of medical education in the District had deprived many of clinical facilities and opportunities for teaching. The new Medical School leased a building on F Street next to the corner of 12th Street and started the construction of a six-bed infirmary and a dispensary. The first course of lectures began in April, 1851. Columbian now had a vigorous competitor in its own territory. The years immediately before and during the Civil War imposed special problems, but by the time Reconstruction got under way, the two schools had reached a basis of cooperation and through a consultative committee were dealing jointly with common problems.[9]

The annual appropriation by Congress for the Infirmary, which was first authorized in 1848, brought at least temporary relief in a period of great anxiety. On November 1, 1847, the faculty had been informed by its special committee just what the financial situation was. During the period that the Sisters had been in charge the Infirmary had been self-supporting and had had a slight operating surplus; but there was an old debt incurred by the College and Infirmary that amounted to $405.09, providing all outstanding pledges and assessments were paid, which was very unlikely. This could be liquidated by a $50 assessment against each faculty member. Other debts more recently incurred, it was hoped, might be met by the matriculation and graduation fees paid during the next session. If that did not work out, the committee recommended that the institution (i.e., the Infirmary) be suspended in the spring (of 1848), the furniture sold, the debt paid with the proceeds, and any unexpended balance applied to the improvement of the College and Museum. The Sisters were told that the Infirmary would be closed March 1 unless something favorable to the finances happened. It did not happen in time and the Sisters left, but not for long. For as soon as the appropriation was voted, the Mother Superior at Emmitsburg gave her assurance that the Sisters would return as soon as arrangements could be made. Meanwhile a matron was to be appointed, for as a condition for receiving the appropriation the College had to post a bond for $4,000 to insure that twelve beds would be ready at all times for government patients.[10]

The faculty had become very much concerned about finances. An additional assessment of $85 was levied on each member of the faculty to clear up some old outstanding obligations of the Medical College. In theory at least there would then be a surplus of $8.42. Properly contrite over their easy methods of buying on credit in the past, they agreed that all purchases hereafter would be by cash. A secretary of the faculty, George Poore, was appointed at a salary of $25 per quarter to assist the dean in his account-keeping. From time to time efforts were made to keep the accounts of the College and Infirmary separated. Unfortunately they always ended up mingled together as before.[11]

Nothing shows more clearly the proprietary nature of the Medical College and the Infirmary than a situation that was precipitated when Dr. John M. Thomas announced his intention to resign his chair and promised "to furnish the necessary application to the Trustees so soon as he should learn when and how he would be paid for his interest in the building." He was assured that he would be paid a sum equal to his assessments for the new building in annual installments of over $200, unless the

College or Infirmary were discontinued. In that event, when the furniture and equipment were sold, the proceeds should be so distributed that the other members of the faculty would receive a share equal to what Dr. Thomas had previously been paid, after which the balance would be equally divided. On second thought, however, the faculty assessed each member $50 and paid Dr. Thomas $300 in full. Four months later $500 was appropriated to pay each of the chairs $100 as partial reimbursement for assessments previously made for the Infirmary. On May 1, 1850, the sum of $600 was fixed as the amount of each professor's share in the stock of the College and Infirmary, and the dean was directed to give each one a certificate of his share in the stock, under his signature, countersigned by the chairman.[12]

An important change in financial policy was taking place. While no steps had apparently been taken to formalize legally either status, the faculty of the Medical Department had, roughly speaking, operated as a partnership, share and share alike. Now, again roughly speaking, it was operating as a corporation, with some of its personnel both shareholders and teachers, others only teachers. By action of the faculty in March, 1847, the Medical Department was thereafter called "The National Medical School." When resignations were offered and vacancies filled, adjustment of the individual's "interests in the Institution" became an essential fact of each faculty change. Such adjustments often involved considerable complexity. One case will be cited by way of illustration.

The Anatomical Museum was owned by the professors of anatomy and physiology. When in 1854 the professor of physiology resigned, the dean was directed to pay him $150 for his half-ownership of the Museum, arranging at the same time for legal conveyance of the Museum by the professors of anatomy and physiology to the stockholding members of the faculty, excluding the chair of chemistry. The incoming professor of chemistry at the time was not a physician but a chemist and therefore as a layman was estopped from buying into the enterprise.[13]

The middle 'fifties were a period of some difficulty. The faculty agreed to suspend lectures for the 1856-1857 session, permitting three of the professors to lecture to a private class at the Infirmary during the winter months and extending to them the use of the dissecting room. Arrangements were made for the resumption of lectures the following year. There were no graduates in 1857, but in 1858 the graduating class was back to normal size.[14]

The reasons for the sudden and short-lived slump in student enrollment are not fully apparent. It is true that a second and competing medical school had been opened in the District. There is some evidence of internal difficulty. It was reported to the faculty that someone in the Infirmary was discouraging students from remaining by saying that enough students would not be available to justify giving the lectures. A committee appointed to investigate found the originator of the damaging statements, interviewed him, concluded that he acted from misinformation and not malice, and declared the case closed. It was perhaps to reassure the students that shortly after the new session began, they were the College's guests at an evening collation held in the Museum.[15]

Caution justified the new financial dispensation that was established in continuing for a year at least. At the close of each lecture, the professor was to sign his name in a register kept by the dean. In lieu of the sale of tickets, the proceeds from which had gone directly to the professor, the dean was henceforth to sell all tickets and put the fees in a "common fund." At the end of the month, each professor would present to the dean a statement of the number of lectures given, for which he would be paid $5 per lecture. As the session drew to a close in the winter of 1858, the faculty found that they could not "fulfill the requisitions of the $160 fee" and voted to refund to each student any amount he had paid over and above the customary fee of $95 for the lectures.[16]

At the time that Congress was being petitioned for annual appropriations for the relief of the Infirmary, the first major change in curriculum was made when the faculty at its meeting in May, 1848, accepted the rules recently adopted at a conference of the National Medical Society in Baltimore and recommended to the various medical schools. These rules were made effective in the annual circular for the 1848-1849 session. The term of lectures was increased to five months. Daily or weekly examinations were given during the session. In place of the usual thesis, "5 cases of disease were to be observed and written by the candidate himself." During the examinations a number of medical men not connected with the College were to be present, and without their approval no candidate would be passed. Each student was obliged to remain in attendance throughout the entire course of lectures.[17]

Nine years later the faculty directed that the circular for 1857-1858 announce the substitution of Hospital medical instruction in lieu of private medical instruction, and the foundation of a Medical College Library. Because of a lack of proper housing, many of the books which the College had acquired were stored at the Smithsonian Institution through the courtesy of Professor Joseph Henry.[18]

The hours of the lecture schedule had varied little during the history of the College, falling within the forenoon and early afternoon. Significantly enough, it was decided that the winter lectures should be in the afternoon, "provided there are 5 clerks in attendance." The schedule of lectures for 1858-1859 fixed them at hours between 4 and 8 P.M., six days a week, with clinical lectures by the professors of medicine and surgery at some morning hour, at least one lecture per week. The fee of $5 per lecture still obtained. The scheduling of classes in the late afternoon or evening was to be of great significance in the future.[19]

A problem that was to be presented in much more compelling form a faculty on October 5, 1855:
few decades later was introduced by the following letter, laid before the

Thomas Miller, M.D.

Sir:
I am requested by two ladies of New York to inquire if female students would be admitted to the College.
Do me the favor to answer the query at your earliest convenience.
With sentiments of respect and esteem.
Yours truly,
Julia Keep

By way of reply, the dean quoted to Mrs. Keep the resolution adopted by the faculty:

Resolved, that the Dean be instructed to inform Mrs. Keep who has applied in regard to the admission of Female Students to attend the lectures of the National Medical College—that the faculty respectfully decline to receive them.[20]

Dr. Toner in his *Anniversary Oration* eloquently describes the way in which the Infirmary justified the confidence and support of the public. Although occupying government property and assisted in large measure by government subsidy, the faculty was jealous in safeguarding the use of their facilities for only those purposes for which the Infirmary had been turned over to the College. When they were asked if they would permit the use of the Infirmary as a shelter should the troops in attendance upon the laying of the cornerstone of the Washington Monument (July 4, 1848) be forced to leave their tents because of inclement weather, permission was refused. On the other hand, a few months later, when the Board of Health asked if the Infirmary could be used for cholera patients "should it visit our city," cooperation on a major scale was immediately forthcoming. The faculty agreed to equip the upper story of the West Wing to accommodate 25 cholera patients referred to the Infirmary by the Board of Health. The Infirmary would furnish all medicine, diet, and necessary and proper medical attention at a charge of $5 per week, to begin with the first patient and continue until the death or discharge of the last. Additional beds would be furnished at the same rate. The faculty was ready to admit some patients gratuitously. One member of the Board would sign for the admission of each patient and the Board would pay for nurses and the burial of the dead.[21]

The well-justified confidence of the public of a growing city in the institution soon taxed its facilities so severely that expansion was necessary. In 1852, Drs. Thomas Miller, Grafton Tyler, William P. Johnston, J. F. May, and R. K. Stone, all of them members of the faculty, petitioned Congress for assistance. Their cause was espoused by Congressman Edward Stanly of North Carolina, who succeeded in tacking on to an appropriations law an amendment which granted $20,000 "to enlarge the accommodations for the benefit of the sick and the treatment of paupers." As soon as funds were available the project was started and the work of remodeling and enlargement was pushed forward under the supervision of the building committee: Drs. Miller, May, and Johnston.

The press described the remodeled structure in laudatory terms. Reporting on an official inspection by the Secretary of the Interior, the *Washington News* for November 13, 1853, said that that official and his party had been much pleased.

The ground on which the Infirmary and College stand contains several acres, and when improved by the erection of fences and the removal of the old jail, will form one of the ornaments of the city. No dwelling houses are in the immediate vicinity, and no persons having contagious diseases are admitted to the institution. On this account it retains its location in the region of the City Hall, so as to accommodate all of the citizens who may be injured suddenly, and cannot bear to be carried to any remote spot, or who may require speedy medical assistance.

Removed as it was from the noise and confusion of the city streets, the location was ideal.

While from the beginning of the institution's management it had served as a marine hospital for the care of disabled seamen sent to it by the collectors of customs at Georgetown and Alexandria, its service as an emergency hospital had also elicited much favorable comment. One enthusiastic observer declared that no sooner did an injury or illness occur on the streets, than the resident students appeared with a litter to carry the patient to the Infirmary.

A writer for the *Washington News* on February 21, 1854, stated that, having visited the Infirmary the day before "and examined every apartment and ward in the edifice," he would attempt to describe the improvements. What he wrote is worthy of quotation at some length:

The main building has been raised and an upper story added, the old interior being gutted and better ventilated rooms being substituted for the old ones. In the main building three corridors have been provided, measuring one hundred and sixty-four feet in length and eight feet in width. These corridors, as they are without any obstruction, present a suitable and convenient promenade for convalescent patients. In front of the building a large and imposing portico has been erected, which will afford room enough for the patients in suitable weather to enjoy fresh air outside the Infirmary.

An entirely new brick building has been erected in the rear, measuring twenty-five feet in length and fifty feet in breadth. We understand that this new building is intended for the female department, there being a great number of additional rooms well suited for that purpose. The amphitheatre of the Infirmary is also in the new building on the third floor. It is a long room about fifty feet square, and is lighted from side windows and a large glass skylight. We understand that a medical course of lectures is now being delivered in this spacious apartment, which is well arranged and provided with seats for about three hundred persons. The building is well provided with gas and waterpipes. Each floor is provided with a bathroom and other conveniences suitable for the sick. Speaking tubes and bells have been provided for every story, and nothing indeed seems to have been overlooked, that is likely to promote the comfort of the inmates. The building is well heated in every part of it, by three of Chilson's large furnaces.

While everything has been done in the interior of the building to render it neat, comfortable, and commodious, its exterior appearance has not been neglected. It has a handsome and improved front, the portico to which we have alluded being a prominent feature.

There were available more than 100 completely finished rooms with accommodations for at least 300 persons in the enlarged Infirmary.[22]

The faculty was sufficiently pleased to order an engraving on wood of the Infirmary building at a cost not to exceed $30. Three years later the woodcut was ordered electrotyped, thus creating what came to be used as the official illustration of the Washington Infirmary.[23]

Reference was made earlier to the avowed effort to keep separately the financial accounts of the College and the Infirmary. Any success along this line was far from complete. Each year a faculty committee reported on the dean's accounts. These reports dealt with both the College and the Hospital without any consistent breakdown as between the two. To give here any appearance of consistency of procedure would be to belie the facts, yet some general tendencies seem to emerge. The dean had under his control the funds derived from the sale of student tickets. Out of these funds he paid the faculty ($5 per lecture usually) and the costs of running the college—maintenance, custodial, etc.—but these noninstructional costs were hard to separate from like costs for the Hospital quartered in the same structure. The cost of some instructional materials and needed readjustment in the teaching area was paid, by appropriation, from the dean's funds. Other costs of this same character were taken care of by what was called "a tax." The leading example of this was the cost of chemicals and breakage which was defrayed by a 20 per cent, later lowered to 10 per cent, tax on the total sale of tickets of the chair of chemistry. From time to time, about once a year, holders of the stock of the institution were paid $100 each. This, which could just as easily be rationalized as a dividend paid to stockholders, was considered as indemnification for assessments previously paid.

There was, however, another aggregate of moneys separate from the dean's fund. This apparently included what was referred to from time to time in making appropriations as "funds in the hands of the Curator." This second group of funds included what was received from pay patients, marine patients, the government fund, and other sources, and, in general terms, was applied to the expenses of the Infirmary. When the report was made by the faculty committee, on at least one occasion the joint deficit of the College and Infirmary was made up by a $500 appropriation from the government fund. To understand the report, apparently we must assume that only the part of the government subsidy which had been used for the care of the indigent was carried as income. The balance was probably held as a convenient cushion to take care of deficits in operating costs due to other unforeseen (?) emergencies.[24]

Certainly in any matter relating to the Infirmary, the Medical faculty was supreme. It had probably never been doubted in fact; but in the spring of 1860, when a paper was sent to the Board of Trustees of Columbian College asking the Board's intervention because all members of the faculty were not on an equality, it was laid down as a rule: "The Joint Committee [of Faculty and College Trustees] then decided that the Board of Trustees had nothing to do with the Infirmary—it being a private matter."[25]

In the discharge of their duties as administrators of the Infirmary, the members of the faculty appear to have utilized the curator in many ways, striving thus to keep separate the affairs of the College and the Infirmary. This is suggested by the fact that when a letter requesting information was presented at a faculty meeting, "as it referred entirely to matters relating to the Infirmary it was referred to the curator for answer." As stated above, he received and disbursed funds.[26]

In the earlier days of the original Hospital, before the enlargement of 1853, when the number of patients was exceedingly small and the sums to be handled very modest, the Sisters had received funds from patients and made all but what was described as "heavy purchases." When a prosector was appointed in 1858 "to dissect for the chairs of Anatomy and Surgery, make preparations, and mount specimens for the museum," judgment as to the faithful performance of his duties was placed in the hands of the dean and curator, and his compensation of $75 and his expenses were to come from funds in the hands of the dean. Here, for obvious reasons, the line was not drawn sharply between the College and the Infirmary. The same was true when the operation of the apothecary shop was put under the supervision of the professor of chemistry. A committee of the faculty was appointed to draw up rules and regulations and define the duties to be performed by the prosector and curator, but there is no evidence of the report of such a committee being presented to the faculty. It would be of interest in the study of hospital administration.

From time to time in the Medical College's circular, attention would be called to the fact that "Medical students desiring situations as resident students in the Washington Infirmary (which is the clinical part of the National Medical College) are requested to make applications by letter to the Curator. . . . It is unnecessary to state the great advantages of residence in a hospital for clinical instruction. Those making early application will have precedence."[27] In 1855, there was provision for 6 resident students. Two years later, the number was increased to 10.[28]

Speaking but five years after the Washington Infirmary had ceased to exist, Dr. Toner in his *Anniversary Oration* of 1866 referred to the enviable reputation that this institution had achieved:

The institution was conducted with liberality to the poor, enlightened judgment, and professional ability, and was of incalculable usefulness in the relief of suffering, by the accommodation it afforded to strangers and others compelled to resort to such an establishment. Its central position and large, airy rooms, with the assiduous attention given to patients by physicians and nurses, made it popular with the public and the profession.[29]

It was providential that such an institution did exist. In spite of the inevitable logic which had long pointed to civil war, Washington, located on the borderline between the two contestants, was in no way prepared for the outbreak of hostilities. The people of the city itself were mixed in their allegiance. The city was totally undefended. It was certainly not prepared to take care of war's gruesome carnage. When, in the rush of units to the defense of Washington, the Sixth Massachusetts Regiment reached Baltimore, it was overwhelmed and badly mauled by hostile mobs. The regiment's many casualties were brought on to Washington and taken to the Washington Infirmary.[30]

It was a great misfortune for the Medical College and for the community that the Washington Infirmary, being the only available hospital in the District, was requisitioned for military use in April, 1861, as the first casualties began to pour into the city. It served as a military hospital for only six months, for on November 4, 1861, a disastrous fire destroyed the building.

By the middle of October a building on E Street, between 11th and 12th Streets, known as the Union Printing Office or the Constitution Office, had been rented and the dean authorized to fix up the building so as to suit the purposes of the faculty.[31]

The last class graduated while the College was located in the Infirmary was, like those of the years immediately preceding, abnormally large, averaging over 25. There were, however, only 6 graduates in 1862 and 12 the following year. It was, therefore, not surprising that in consequence of the small number of students lectures were suspended for the session of 1863-1864.

There were many causes for this falling-off in students. The loss of the Infirmary had been disturbing and, to an extent, demoralizing. There was another medical school in the District which had been able to continue without any comparable loss. Columbian College in all of its branches had in the years before the Civil War drawn many students from the South: they had gone home. Due to war conditions, staffing the faculty was difficult. The faculty had always remained amazingly constant in its personnel. Now there seemed to be perpetual flux. Chairs would be joined so that one man could take over the lectures of a resigned or absent colleague in addition to his own. In some cases the number of lectures had been radically reduced by sheer necessity. The faculty in a formal resolution declaring that "the present and future standing of the National Medical College have been placed in jeopardy," resolved "that we should at once put an end to what may justly be considered as a ground of complaint." The resignation of one professor who had been particularly culpable in failing to deliver half of his scheduled lectures was immediately demanded. Three months later the lectures for 1863-1864 were suspended.[32]

In the report of this action in the *Minutes* of the Board of Trustees, among "various unfavorable causes" for the radical shrinkage of the student body, emphasis is placed on the impression that had spread that the government was going to open a school for gratuitous medical and surgical instruction. It is a fair supposition that what was referred to was a military course under the Surgeon General of the Army. The faculty instructed its chairman on July 24, 1863, to confer with the Surgeon General to see "whether our students would be admitted to their military course, and if so, upon what terms." No record of an answer to the inquiry is available. Acquiescing in the faculty's decision, the Board expressed the opinion that possibly the work of the School might be resumed under more favorable auspices.[33]

When lectures in the Medical College were suspended, the Civil War was half over. The "more favorable auspices" under which lectures might be resumed obviously involved the restoration of peace. Deprived at the outbreak of war of its use of the excellent facilities which the Washington Infirmary had offered and without a real base for its operation, the National Medical College was hardly equipped as a college to play a large role in the city. In fact, more interest in medical matters attached to College Hill, where two large hospitals—Columbian College General Hospital and Carver General Hospital—were located throughout the war period. Many medical men connected with the National Medical College as individuals held key positions.

It appears that at least 46 medical graduates served in the Union Army and 24 in the Confederate forces. William James Hamilton White (1827-1862), M.D. 1848, who spent his professional career as a surgeon in the Army, fell at Antietam September 17, 1862, the first medical officer killed in the Civil War. Apparently the only medical graduate to serve at Columbian College General Hospital was Marcellus King Moxley (1838-1889), M.D. 1863. Beginning the study of medicine with his father at Wheelersburg, Ohio, in 1859, he attended his first course of lectures at the Cleveland Medical College in 1860-1861. He came to Washington in 1861, was admitted to the Medical Cadet Corps, and attended lectures at the National Medical College, 1862-1863. Dr. Moxley was commissioned in 1868.

Dr. Robert King Stone (1822-1872), a member of the Medical faculty, 1848-1859, was the personal physician of President Lincoln.[34]

Dr. Alexander Yelverton Peyton Garnett (1820-1888), Professor of Anatomy, 1848-1849, and of Clinical Medicine, 1858-1861, and later for about two years, resigning in 1870, Professor of the Practice of Medicine, was the personal physician of President Jefferson Davis and General Robert E. Lee and his family. He spent the war years in Richmond where as Surgeon C.S.A. he was in charge of military hospitals. Determining at the outbreak of the Civil War to follow the dictates of his conscience and support the cause of his native Virginia, he abandoned his lucrative practice in Washington. When he found his exit blocked by the closure of the Long Bridge, he made a personal appeal to Simon Cameron, Secretary of War, for a passport to Virginia. The Secretary tried to dissuade him from going by every argument that he could muster, but to no avail. "If you offered me a lump of gold as large as the dome of the Capitol, I would not do it," was Garnett's reply when Cameron urged him to stay. He followed the Confederacy to its end, even accompanying President Davis when Richmond was evacuated. In the fall of 1865, he was back in Washington and resumed the distinguished career which had been interrupted by his service to the Confederacy. In 1887, Dr. Garnett was elected president of the American Medical Association. "He was strong-willed, of good education, large acquaintance, and captivating address; had an excellent and discriminating mind, with a store of common sense, an untiring energy, and a sympathetic nature"—such was Busey's estimate of Dr. Garnett.[35]

Dr. John G. F. Holston (1809-1874), Professor of Surgery, 1858-1861, and Dr. Joseph H. Warren, Professor of Anatomy, 1862-1863, were surgeons, U.S.A., during the Civil War.[36] John Frederick May (1812-

1891), A.B. 1831, M.D. 1834, at first professor of anatomy and then of surgery, 1839-1858, who identified the body of John Wilkes Booth, is said to have been called for consultation to the bedside of the dying Lincoln.

A reconstruction of the events of the tragic day of the President's assassination places a graduate of the Medical College in the theater box where the President lay shortly after the fatal shot. That physician was A. F. A. King (1841-1914), M.D. 1861, for thirty-seven years professor of obstetrics. The first physician to reach the box to take charge was only twenty-three, the third physician, Dr. King, twenty-four years old. Responsibility was riding heavily on the shoulders of youth that night.[37]

Dr. King, who had been seated in the orchestra of Ford's Theatre, climbed into the President's box, tried to revive the wounded man, and then helped carry him to the house of William Petersen, 516 10th Street. The young physician was just beginning a half-century of practice in Washington. English by birth, he had come to this country with his family as a boy of ten. He was graduated in medicine from the National Medical College at the age of twenty. Although not an officer in either army, he treated Confederate wounded in Virginia during the early part of the war, and later, Union wounded in Washington. Continuing his medical training, he received the M.D. degree from the University of Pennsylvania in 1865. Perhaps no other man had longer tenure of a chair in the Medical College than he had of the chair of obstetrics, and few have been as vividly remembered. In the field of his specialty he wrote a highly useful *Manual of Obstetrics*, first published in 1882 and going through frequent editions. His forte was teaching. Large in frame, tending to be obese, always meticulously attired and highly articulate, he was a person to be remembered. Apt in characterization, vivid in the dramatization of his material, and skillful in the organization of his lectures, he attempted and succeeded admirably in his desire to give his students a sound and basic understanding of elementary obstetrics.

But aside from the subject he taught, his vigorous and active mind ranged widely over the whole field of medicine, sometimes to extents where he apparently had few followers. One of his papers delivered before the Philosophical Society in 1882 and published in abridged form in *The Popular Science Monthly* a year and a half later under the less forbidding title of "Insects and Disease—Mosquitos and Malaria" has secured for him a significant place in medical science. Two features of this paper are important, its date and its careful and rational presentation of the material. Recognizing the work of many predecessors in the study of the transmission of disease by insects and utilizing their findings, he marshaled his information about malaria and mosquitoes in support of his contention. Fifteen years were to pass before King's theory was proved correct. Others had voiced the theory, but King had gone beyond them and presented a logical and documented case. In the post-Civil War period and during the remainder of the nineteenth century and into the twentieth, Dr. King was an important figure in the affairs of the Medical faculty. He became a tradition even in his own lifetime.[38]

It was unfortunate that the Medical College's occupancy of the Washington Infirmary was of such short duration. The circumstances which had turned the structure over to the faculty were a godsend. The outbreak of the Civil War, which cost the faculty the use of its teaching Hospital and which forced the Medical College to suspend its lectures for two years, was almost catastrophic in effect. During the years when the faculty had operated the Infirmary and the Dispensary connected with it, wide public acceptance had been won and the Medical College had played a major part in the institutional life of the city. The acceptance by the Congress of the duty of aiding the indigent sick by annual appropriation had established an important policy of government support. The course of study underwent its first major change. Requirements for the degree were raised, the length of the session extended, and the curriculum enriched by the establishment of new chairs. There was wide experimentation to determine the best time in the day for lectures. The most significant change, with the resources in hand, was the constant expansion of clinical teaching. It can be seen in formal faculty regulations, in the increased scheduling of clinical classes, and, in a rather dramatic way, in what happened to the old graduation requirement that "all inaugural dissertations," as they were often called, had to be written. This dissertation, dealing usually with an account of some disease, was not only a medical exercise but a literary effort. Frequently theses were rejected because of grammatical and rhetorical deficiency. In its place, what? The writing up of a required number of cases. The literary touch of the classical age had gone, the clinical age had dawned.

PART TWO

Midtown (The Century on H Street)

CHAPTER SIX

The Corcoran Gift

In the post-bellum period, great changes took place in every aspect of the Columbian College and of its Medical Department, the National Medical College, and in the organizational relationship of the medical unit to its parent institution. From the founding through the period of the War of 1861-1865, that relationship had been limited in degree to those contacts necessitated by the Medical Department's dependence on the charter of 1821 for a legal base. Under that charter, Columbian College had instituted a Medical Department, approved a set of ordinances for its governance, and imposed upon it complete responsibility for its finances. Because its faculty were members of the total faculty of Columbian College, it approved their appointments on the nomination of the Medical faculty; and because its degrees were degrees of Columbian College, they were conferred by Columbian College. The relation approached being only a formal one. Financial autonomy expressed itself in freedom from all intervention of the mother institution in the internal affairs of the Medical Department. As its history indicates, it was, in a real sense, the property of the Medical faculty.

The relationship was illustrated by the fact that the College was located on College Hill, north of the boundary; the Medical School, as required by the ordinances, in the very heart of the city. The old Medical College at 10th and E Streets was built and maintained by the Medical faculty at its own expense. The Washington Infirmary in Judiciary Square was assigned by an act of Congress not to the College, but to the Medical faculty, and was improved, equipped, and maintained by them. In this period of marked change about to be described, the Medical College was located in a building given not to it, but to Columbian College, the mother institution.

When it started out on H Street, the relations, with the exception of a change in landlord, were about the same as they had been. By a curious interplay of circumstances, central control, not wholly without opposition, was gradually and persistently asserted. With the revival of the Law Department at this time, a second professional school was brought into the College system. The coming of Dr. James C. Welling to the presidency of Columbian College in 1871 brought to the institution a man of great educational vision. The sights of the institution were raised. Graduate work and research, technical courses, courses for employed students—all were involved in what came to be called "The University Plan." A change in the charter created a Columbian University as the successor of the old Columbian College, with a complete university organization and mission indicated. The geography of the institution was made to conform to the same concept. Gradually, all of the branches of the University were brought into the same area: the Preparatory School and the Medical School on H Street between 13th and 14th Streets, the Law School and University Hall on H Street between 14th and 15th Streets. When, due to the financial crisis of 1910, the University sold University Hall and the Law School, the Medical School remained on H Street in the location it occupied for more than a century.[1]

When the government requisitioned the Washington Infirmary at the outbreak of the Civil War, the lectures for the 1860-1861 session were completed. In the fall of that year, the faculty rented a building on E Street between 11th and 12th Streets known as the Constitution or Union Office (these were names of a paper printed at this place). The dean was authorized to fit the building to suit the purposes of the faculty.[2] The exact extent of the occupation of this building is unknown. Dr. Toner, in his *Anniversary Oration,* says lectures were continued there "for sometime."[3] Apparently, Commencement was held there on Thursday, March 6, 1862.[4] On June 23, 1863, President Samson reported to the Board of Trustees that the Medical faculty was occupying rooms in the old Trinity Church, soon to be refitted and used as the Law School.[5]

Just where the intimation ever came from that would point the way to the future is not recorded. The first mention is in the *Minutes* of the Medical faculty for its meeting of April 1, 1862:

On motion, Professor Schaeffer was appointed a committee to wait on Mr.

Cochran [sic], and ascertain, if his building on H Street could be obtained for the use of the faculty, and if so, upon what terms.

The next reference appears in the records of the Trustees. Reporting to the Board of Trustees of Columbian College on June 24, 1862, President Samson referred to the troubles of the Medical College in the many changes in faculty that were occurring and to the falling off of students due to the war. He stated hopefully that prospects had been improved by the news that "a gentleman of this city" was considering the gift of a building to the College for the use of the Medical School. It may be surmised that this pleasant news was due, at least in part, to overtures made to Mr. Corcoran by Professor Schaeffer in accordance with the Medical faculty's resolution of April 1, 1862. A significant resolution was adopted by the Trustees at the same meeting. A committee was directed to consider the question of more direct control by the Board of the affairs of the National Medical College, especially if any building was *given to the College* for the use of the Medical Department.[6]

The hoped-for donor referred to by Professor Schaeffer was W. W. Corcoran, the great Washington banker and philanthropist, Trustee from 1869 to 1888, and president of the corporation, 1869-1888. He was the University's most liberal benefactor during the nineteenth century; his support made possible the inauguration of Welling's "University Plan." The building referred to was on the Medical School site which was to be occupied for over a century. The structure had probably been planned for a library, at least it is so described in a letter of Mr. Corcoran.[7] It was, however, to serve a totally different purpose.

The Army Medical Museum was founded in 1862 "to preserve the medical experience of the Civil War." Specimens were collected on the battlefield and shipped to Washington in barrels of whiskey to be mounted for display either in alcohol or dry.[8] Mr. Corcoran's building was taken by the War Department and turned over to the Surgeon General of the Army to house the Army Medical Museum.

Dr. Ralph Walsh, Acting Assistant Surgeon, U.S.A., who was placed in immediate charge of the Museum, described the institution as he found it:

Said Museum, when I assumed charge, consisted of two large rooms filled with empty cases, a back building in which was stored a large number of dry and moist specimens in barrels and alcohol, to be mounted by Mr. Schafhirt, who was employed for that purpose. There was also a mass of written histories,

numbered to correspond with the specimens. Under my supervision the specimens were mounted, numbered and placed in the cases, and the histories con-
densed and recorded. In other words, I think I can make a just claim, though
I have never heretofore done so, to have started the Army Medical Museum. I
mention as a possibly interesting fact, that most of the alcohol used for the
preservation of the moist specimens was procured by distillation of contraband
liquors seized on the Long Bridge. These liquors ran from beer and blackberry
wine to straight alcohol, and were packed in many peculiar vessels. Frequently
women were arrested with belts under their skirts, to which were attached tin
sectional cans holding from a quart to a gallon, and, in a number of cases,
false breasts, each holding a quart or more.[9]

In the summer of 1865, Anthony Hyde, Mr. Corcoran's agent and
general representative, informed the Board of Trustees that the building would be presented to Columbian College, and President Samson
reported the good news to the Medical faculty.[10] The next problem was
to get the Museum out of the building so that it could be used for educational purposes. The arrangement of the building was placed in the
hands of the Medical faculty. The Board, assured that the Museum
would be moved as soon as its new quarters were ready, announced that
at its next meeting it would fix the terms of the lease to the Medical
faculty.[11]

Secretary of War Stanton, however, declined to give immediate occupancy and the faculty reconciled itself to meeting in the Law building
for the 1865-1866 session. During that year there were 17 students in
attendance, four of whom received their degrees at the 1866 Commencement. From then on the enrollment steadily increased: 1866 to 1867, 29;
1867 to 1868, 35; 1868 to 1869, 60; 1869 to 1870, 70. Reaching that high
point in registration, an average student body of 50 was maintained during
the 1870's. In 1872, there were 6 graduates in Pharmacy, each having
served an apprenticeship in the drug and apothecary business and having
taken two courses of lectures.[12]

While the Medical faculty was waiting for the Army Medical Museum
to move from the H Street building, the Trustees of Columbian College
in a body called on Mr. Corcoran, on his return after spending the latter
years of the war abroad, to welcome him home and express their thanks
for his many acts of benevolence. Mr. Corcoran was greatly touched and
in moving terms thanked his old friends for their true estimate of his
motives.[13]

After considerable pressure had been brought to bear, the Surgeon

The Reverend George Whitefield Samson, D.D., Fifth President of the University, 1859-1871.

James Clarke Welling, Sixth President of the University, 1871-1894.

William Wilson Corcoran, President of the Corporation, 1869-1888. Among his many benefactions was the gift of the original Medical School property on H Street.

Edward T. Fristoe, A.M., Phar.D., LL.D., Professor of Chemistry, 1871-1892.

The Diploma of George C. Samson, M.D., 1867, Signed by His Father, President George W. Samson.

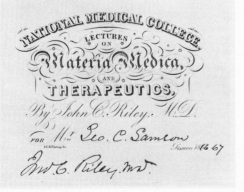

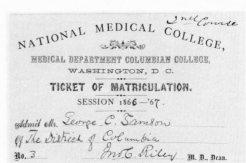

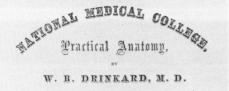

Student Cards of George C. Samson, M.D., 1867, showing that Columbian still followed the traditional form of those issued by the University of Pennsylvania to Dr. Thomas Sewall a half century earlier.

This Structure (*above*), Built by W. W. Corcoran, on the north side of
H Street, between 13th and 14th Streets, was taken over to house the Army
Medical Museum (founded in 1862). Presented by Mr. Corcoran to Columbian College in 1865, it was turned over to the Medical Department when
relinquished by the Museum in 1866. In 1868 and again in 1887 major improvements involving radical enlargement were authorized. In this modified form
(*below*), the building was used until 1902.

William P. Johnston, M.D., President of the Faculty, 1855-1856, 1857-1860, 1874-1876; Professor of Surgery, 1842-1845, of Obstetrics, 1849-1859, 1865-1876.

Grafton Tyler, M.D., Professor of Theory and Practice of Medicine, 1846-1859; Dean, 1852-1853.

Albert Freeman Africanus King, M.D., Professor of Obstetrics, 1871-1913; Dean, 1879-1894.

Daniel Kerfoot Shute, M.D., Professor of Anatomy, 1887-1888; Dean, 1894-1897.

The First Hospital on H Street. Built in 1882 for the Preparatory School (later known as Columbian Academy) and, when the Academy was discontinued, remodeled for use as a hospital and opened in 1898 *(above)*. It was connected with the newly constructed hospital immediately east of it in 1902 *(below)*. The views of the interior on the following page are taken from the annual catalogues, 1900 to 1902: *above left*, a ward; *center*, a private room; *below*, the operating room.

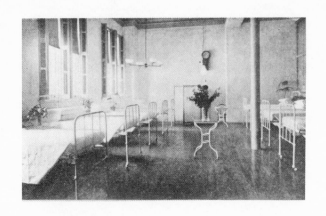

College of Veterinary Medicine, 2113-2115
14th Street, 1908-1918.

College of Pharmacy, 808 Eye Street, 1906-
1919.

David Eastburn Buckingham, D.V.M., Dean
of the College of Veterinary Medicine.

Henry E. Kalusowski, M.D., Phar.D., Dean
of the College of Pharmacy.

General informed President Samson, who in turn notified the Medical faculty that the lecture room would be given up by the Army by November 1, 1866. It was immediately decided to delay the opening of the 1866-1867 session until that day. On Thursday evening, November 1, 1866, at seven o'clock Colonel James L. Edwards, president of the Board of Trustees of Columbian College, formally turned the keys over to Dr. Miller, president of the Medical faculty, thus inaugurating the use of the building for Medical education.[14]

CHAPTER SEVEN

Relocation

J ust as the Medical College was moving, for the first time in its history, into a building owned by Columbian College, a sharp, and perhaps not unexpected, confrontation occurred between the College Board of Trustees and the Medical faculty. As noted above, the Board had appointed a committee on June 22, 1862, to consider the question of more direct control of the affairs of the Medical Department, particularly if any building given to Columbian College was turned over to the Medical faculty for its use. The special condition having arisen, the Board was apparently ready to act and the action came quite naturally.

In the ordinances drawn up for the reestablished Law School, it was provided that professors be elected annually at the regular April meeting of the Board of Trustees. Secretary Robert C. Fox now notified the Medical faculty that the Board was applying this rule to all faculties. The faculty met the proposal with unyielding opposition and asked that the action be rescinded. President Samson agreed to present the faculty's case to the Trustees and "ascertain their motives." In two days' time, the dean had a letter from President Samson.

Dr. Samson said that the move was not directed against any individual in particular. Since the Medical Department no longer occupied a building furnished and maintained by the faculty, it was proper that the Medical faculty be treated in a uniform fashion with the College and Law faculties. Besides, the president observed, he had heard of cases in the past where difficulty had arisen because professors were "incompetent or inattentive." "The privilege of nomination has always been allowed and, I am sure, will always be to the faculties themselves." The president had not yet had all his say. He referred to an impression that the medical faculty made a mistake in intermitting for two years their lectures, thus giving the other college, heretofore inferior, superior credit for determination and perseverance. This however I have found attributed to the fault of the times, rather than of the men engaged.

The president advised the faculty to go on as if nothing of the action of the Board of Trustees was intended as special to them. To do otherwise would profit no one, but he would help in any way he could.

The faculty was not placated. Its members voted to send "their united resignations" to the Board. President Samson met with the faculty, asked them to withdraw their resignations, and stated that he thought a majority of the Board was not satisfied with the "obnoxious" resolution and that he would bring his influence to bear on them. The faculty agreed that if a majority of the Board would sign a paper undertaking to vote for a repeal of the action at the next Trustees' meeting, the resignations would be withdrawn. President Samson met with the faculty the next day, presented the required paper, the resignations were withdrawn, and a protest against the original action ordered made to the Trustees at their next meeting. At the same meeting the dean was directed by the faculty to inform the professor of obstetrics and the diseases of women and children that his resignation "would be acceptable and that the best interests of the faculty would be advanced thereby." Needless to say, the resignation was presented and accepted. It was a strange footnote to President Samson's letter. The crisis had lasted for just a week. The next day, the building was formally turned over to the Medical College. All was sweetness and light.[1]

No sooner were the new quarters occupied than the faculty set about a reorganization of its program. After full consideration by a special committee, the length of the regular session was fixed to run from the Monday nearest or next after October 15 until March 1, with four lectures daily, six days a week. The faculty was to be made up of those who, having served with honor, had been designated as emeriti, and nine active professors, holding the following chairs: obstetrics and the diseases of women and children; materia medica and therapeutics; special operative and clinical surgery; theory and practice of medicine; chemistry; physiology, pathology, and medical jurisprudence; general military surgery and hygiene; anatomy; and clinical medicine. The first eight full courses would include not less than 40 nor more than 48 lectures. Clinical medicine was to be given not less than once nor more than three times a week at such times that there would be no conflict with the regular lectures. Compensation was to be prorated. The previous arrangement whereby adjuncts had been permitted to deliver lectures during the regular winter course was abolished, and those listed at the time as adjuncts were to be constituted quiz officers of the College. Professors not resident in Washington (two of them were not) were to be permitted so to arrange their lectures that, in any event, they would not be required to stay in Washington longer than half the term. One of the nonresident faculty stated that he could not continue to serve unless he was paid for his extra expenses of transportation. During the first month of the term, the dean was to report to the faculty on funds in hand and was to make a division of them as fixed by the faculty. At the end of the term, after funds to meet current expenses had been set aside, the remainder was to be divided among the faculty. No promissory notes were to be taken for tickets, cash only was to be accepted, and unless by faculty vote no free tickets were to be given. All fees for partial courses were to go into the "general fund," that is, the fund held for maintenance and administrative expenses. Regular meetings of the faculty were to be held monthly.[2]

As part of the reorganization, it was decided to hold each year spring and summer courses, three months in length, beginning April 1. These courses were entirely distinct from the regular ones during the fall and winter. Three lectures were held each day, beginning at 6 P.M. The course included 36 lectures on anatomy; another course by some other member of the faculty, not necessarily on the same topic each year, to be given by an outside lecturer, if no regular teacher desired to give it; and six courses of 24 hours each on special topics given by other than members of the regular faculty. Each lecturer was authorized to issue tickets for his course. The topics for the 1867 short session were: Anatomy and Histology (Thompson); Botany (Schaeffer); Physiology (Lee); Diseases of Children (Middleton); Thoracic Diseases (Young); Fractures and Dislocations (Todd); New Remedies (King); Diagnosis in Special Diseases (King).[3]

These rather elaborate, and interesting, offerings were made possible by the fact that the Medical College now had use of the entire building. The blackboards and cases which had been in the Museum were bought by the College, and workmen from the Army Quartermasters' Department had put the interior of the building back in shape, as fully as possible in its previous condition. The keys were delivered to President Samson early in December, 1866.[4] The Trustees had given the Medical faculty full authority to fix the building for its effective use. The Museum cases were put in the lower lecture room and the front part of the upper lecture room was fitted as an amphitheater, large enough to accommodate the whole student body, and equipped with gas fixtures for anatomical purposes. By way of happy augury, the Medical College operated in the black for the 1867-1868 session, with income of $2,420; expenses, $2,192.29; and a balance of $227.71.[5] President Samson reported to his Board of Trustees that "by immemorial usage" the income of the Medical College had been divided among its faculty.[6] The outlook seemed bright, and in a roseate glow of optimism faculty and students sat down to a festive dinner on February 22, 1868, provided at a cost of $100 from the funds of the Medical College.[7]

In late August 1868, it was announced in the press that:

The Trustees of the Columbian College have adopted the plans and specifications for the extension and alteration of the building presented by the committee of the medical faculty, and promptly appropriated the necessary funds for the immediate execution of the work. The improvement will consist of a large and commodious amphitheatre; a spacious, well arranged, and well ventilated room for practical anatomy; a chemical laboratory, to be fitted up and furnished with the necessary apparatus, under the direction of the Professor of Chemistry; rooms for the practice of the students in the application of bandages and surgical appliances, the use of the microscopes, the practice on the manikin, etc. and the rooms for the dispensary, which is to be speedily organized.[8]

One item in the press story just quoted needs clarification: that is the reference to the Trustees' prompt appropriation of the necessary funds. The flurry over the annual election of professors had, perhaps, caused the Trustees to delay the implementation of their announced policy of extending greater control over the Medical Department. The old fiscal relations with Columbian College were basically still maintained. President Samson had spoken of the fees as being distributed to the faculty in 1868 "by immemorial usage." When it came to providing funds for the enlargement of the facilities of the Medical College, the negotiations were rather long drawn out. The first proposal was to authorize the changes at a cost not to exceed $5,000, on which sum the faculty was to pay interest at the rate of 6 per cent. A final settlement several months later authorized the expenditure of a sum not to exceed $4,000. This sum, however, was enough to cover construction costs only, and the faculty had had to have gas and water fixtures and sewage arrangements made in addition.[9]

A significant indication that forces of change were at work was seen in the action taken by the faculty in establishing in October, 1868, an executive committee of three with authority to deal with all matters concerning buildings, clinics, and the details of courses. In any case of disagreement, the matter was to be referred to the faculty for settlement. It is quite clear that a new concept of faculty administration was emerging. In the days before the Medical College moved into its new quarters on H Street, when the autonomous and proprietary position of the faculty was unchallenged, questions of administration, as they had arisen, had been referred to small committees, which after investigation made recommendations to the faculty for appropriate action. In this way, as befitted stockholders, the entire group was involved actively in the business of the institution. Now under the resolution of October 6, 1868, an executive committee was created with power to act. The obvious effect was to eliminate the faculty, to an increasing extent, from administrative concerns and confine them more closely to their prime function as teachers. Two months later, the committee, meeting jointly with one from Georgetown Medical School, fixed a uniform schedule of tuition charges for the two schools: price for full courses, $135; single ticket, $20; matriculation fee, $5. Satisfied with this beginning of cooperation, the faculty directed its executive committee to consult with the Georgetown faculty on all matters of common interest to the two Medical Colleges.[10]

Shortly before this principle of consultation had been formalized, an incident occurred which was to furnish a topic for the agenda of the joint Columbian–Georgetown consultative committee. In the *National Intelligencer* for January 11, 1869, appeared the following brief news item:

TRESPASSING

Thomas Karr and Harry Clark were arrested at an early hour yesterday morning by officers of the First Precinct, on the charge of trespassing on the burial ground at the Washington Asylum, and removing two bodies therefrom. Justice Walter imposed a fine of $60 on each of them, which was promptly paid. The driver of the hack was fined $20 for fast driving. The bodies were given in charge of the Intendant of the Asylum, and reburied in the Asylum burial ground.

The news item was discreetly noncommittal as to the institutional affiliation of the accused, but a week later the committee was directed by the Medical faculty to communicate with the proper authorities to see if the fines recently imposed on "the employees of the College" could be remitted. Those in charge of the room for practical anatomy were reminded of

their duty of observing more caution and entire secrecy in the matter of supplying the College with anatomical material. In case of a repetition of the misadventure of January 10, the faculty will not again respond to any call made upon them, but will cast the entire responsibility upon the Demonstrators themselves.[11]

We get an echo from "the misadventure of January 10" in one of an elaborate series of recommendations made by the Columbian–Georgetown consulting committee two months later and adopted *in toto* by the Medical faculty:

The committee recommends to the Demonstrators of the two colleges to employ a Resurrectionist for both institutions, and to act in concert in procuring material; and also not to permit students to accompany the Resurrectionist.

Along with this recommendation went several others. Every student must settle in full with the dean before the course was completed. No back tickets would be sold. Before graduating, all students were required to take demonstrators' tickets for two sessions. Each school would limit beneficiaries to five. Each candidate for graduation must be examined before the whole faculty. Two blackballs would reject, or at the faculty's option a candidate might present himself again for examination any time prior to the Commencement of the Academic Department. The last regulation can be explained by the fact that the medical class usually graduated at the completion of the course, which ended by early spring. The graduation of the Academic Department, occurring a few months later, was the last opportunity for the public conferring of degrees in the year.

The extent to which these regulations were adhered to was shown by the rejection of a student petition asking that the method of examination prescribed be changed. The dean was directed to reply to them "that as it was a joint agreement with another institution, their request could not be granted."[12]

An incident which occurred at this time and is of interest only because of a renewed curiosity about Chinese methods more than a century

later was the extending of an invitation to the Reverend Dr. Peter Parker
to deliver a few lectures upon Chinese surgery and his experiences in
that country.[13]

The resignation of President George Whitefield Samson closed an
era in the life of the College and the Medical Department. His administration had been passed under the shadow of civil war. In character, zeal,
and ability, Samson must be ranked among the greatest presidents of
the institution. Few men have sacrificed as much. He saw his student
body melt away at the approach of war; and when the government took
over College Hill, he found the College almost homeless and all but
forced to suspend its teaching. The sources of income from which he
had gained outside funds from solicitation began to dry up and were
finally denied him. The College plant that was returned to him after the
war and the meager funds at his disposal were woefully inadequate for
the reconditioning of the property and the resumption of a full educational program. Because of staff reduction for economy's sake and as an
incident of war and military service, he found himself carrying the full
burden of administration, academic and financial, aggravated by constant frustration; it would have been a crushing burden to a weaker
man. That was not all he had to bear. As a minister of the Gospel,
and an eloquent preacher, he continued to pursue his calling with zeal.
As a humanitarian, personally acquainted with the leading officers of both
the Union and Confederate governments, he served as the channel for
getting reading materials, messages, and gifts from families across the
lines to the troops who eagerly awaited them. Toward the end of his
administration there was marked tension between president and Trustees
and Dr. Samson resigned. In spite of the stiffened attitude of the Trustees, he could point to real achievements. On the boundary between two
groups of warring states, Samson, by his unquestioned integrity, had held
the confidence of both sides, and used that confidence for their mutual
advantage. He had preserved the College, reestablished the Law School in a
building of its own, and seen the Medical Department housed in College
property. Because of the approach, the course, and the immediate after-
math of the war, his administration had to be largely a holding operation.
Samson was the first to suggest that he had served his time and should
move on.

It was fortunate that there was an able, though different, man to succeed an able man, when a holding operation was no longer necessary, when
advance was the need. James Clarke Welling, sixth president of the

College (1871-1894), was to preside over the transformation of the institution into a university in name, structure, and mission. He was well qualified for the task which he assumed. A well informed and highly articulate journalist, his editorials in the *National Intelligencer* had influenced public policy in a critical period of our national history.[14]

He had been president of St. John's College in Annapolis and was professor of belles-lettres at Princeton at the time of his election to the presidency of Columbian. His effectiveness as president was tremendously enhanced by the personal and financial support of the president of the corporation, W. W. Corcoran. So convinced was he that Dr. Welling's leadership was essential, that Mr. Corcoran made his donation of the Trinidad property for the creation of an endowment contingent upon Dr. Welling's continuance as president. The office of president took on new importance and authority, when, by charter revision, the president was made ex officio a member of the governing board and the head of the institution, rather than the head of the faculty as under the original charter provision. Although a man of wide-ranging ideas, Welling was very much of a realist.

Serious financial troubles had darkened the last years of his predecessor's term and intensified the tensions between president and Board. A change in the executive did not automatically solve the problem. The Medical Department, which since 1847 had borne the clumsy name of "The National Medical College, the Medical Department of Columbian College," then briefly "The Medical School of Columbian College," and finally "The National Medical College of Columbian University," had under the formula then used been generally self-supporting. The Law Department, which had quickly built up a large enrollment which then subsided, had likewise been generally self-supporting, and for a time, quite profitable.

The trouble was mainly with the College, which was gradually withering away. With its dormitory facilities no longer livable, its plant run down, and its equipment outmoded, its location on the outskirts of the city no longer meant idyllic charm and bucolic simplicity, but just plain inconvenience. Employed students had shown an interest, in increasing numbers, in late afternoon classes, but the remote location of the College made attendance difficult. It was the practical Welling's dictum that if students wanted an education and would pay for it, it should be offered where they could get it. This meant a move, and the disposal of College Hill. It meant also the eventual grouping of all of the units on H Street, where, thanks to Mr. Corcoran's generosity, the Medical School already was located. Welling knew where he was going. Washington, he insisted, was no place for a small college. That type of institution could operate with less cost and to better effect somewhere else. Washington demanded a great university where professional training and research of a most advanced nature could be conducted. That meant money, much money.

The institution had some property, but a quick sale would yield a poor return and would not create the modest endowment fund that was needed. After considerable vacillation, its sale was postponed and a loan of $12,000 secured by a mortgage was negotiated to take care of unpaid taxes, which were mounting at the rate of $1,000 a year. The loan bought them time for reorganizing their plans. "Since," said Welling, "we cannot execute what we projected, we must project what we can execute to the extent and compass of our means."[15]

In the decade preceding the Board's declaration of 1881, there were many evidences that, even though the Medical faculty now occupied a college-owned building, in matters of finance the old familiar procedures were being followed. Dividends were still being distributed to the professors: $100 in 1873; $200 in 1875; $500 in 1877; $300 in 1878; $250 in 1879; $200 in 1880. There was no distribution in 1874, funds being allowed to accumulate in a special deposit for materials and equipment. From this fund $100 was placed at the disposal of each professor for supplying his lectures with needed appliances for teaching.[16] The absence of a distribution in 1876 is explained by the unusually large dividend paid the following year.

As Welling began a renewed scrutiny of the institution's finances, the Medical College became involved in an interesting maneuver designed ostensibly to reduce tax charges, but involving a very significant organizational change in the light of the Board's standing intention to exert greater control over that unit. At a special meeting of the Board on March 16, 1881, the following statement was formally adopted: "That the National Medical College, the Medical Department of the University, is hereby declared to be an integral part of the University and that until further notice the salary of each of the Professors of the School be fixed at one dollar per annum."[17]

The financial autonomy of the Medical College was thus formally repudiated. As a proprietary institution it was profit-making and thus subject to taxes, but as an integral part of the University it was nonprofit-making and tax-exempt. This fact was certified to the District government and the Medical College was relieved from future taxes; there was no refund for past taxes paid.[18] Professors were now salaried by the University. Substantial dividends were still paid as before: $120 in 1881; $200 in 1882; $350 in 1883; $425 in 1884; $375 in 1885.[19] According to the letter of the law (for tax purposes, at least) the proprietary age had ended.

A waning of interest on the part of the professors seemed to be indicated by the complaint of the dean that although he had sent out frequent notices of meetings, he had been unable to get a quorum. For this reason he had, with the consent of the Board of Trustees, established a School of Pharmacy and arranged with Dr. Stabler of Alexandria to give a course on botany and pharmacy. It had been customary for the faculty to deal even with minute business details and it seems strange, in the case of such an important matter as the establishment of a new school, that the dean for lack of a quorum had had to take the matter directly to the Trustees.[20]

From the very beginning of the occupancy of the H Street building, there were indications of feeling on the part of the faculty as to the inadequacy of the building. The appointment of a committee on October 20, 1870, "to have a water closet placed *in* the building" illustrates the efforts made to make the building more usable. During the year 1874, examinations of the roof and the upper room by competent builders were a preliminary to a direction to the executive committee to have improvements made "in the manner that they may deem advisable."[21]

Since major expansion was bound to be necessary before too long, the faculty formally brought to the attention of the Board the immediate desirability of acquiring property adjacent to their building to take care of future needs, a formal action taken annually during the next decade.[22]

Another deep concern, frequently expressed, was the maintenance of a more adequate and better-organized Dispensary than before. On October 10, 1874, the Medical faculty authorized the dean to inform the Commissioners of the District of Columbia of their approval of the establishment of a dispensary system "for gratuitous medical assistance to the poor" and assuring them that if such a system were established the faculty would cooperate as individuals and as a body. By way of preparation for such a system, the executive committee was charged to establish immediately a daily dispensary service at the Medical College.

Regulations for the National Medical College Dispensary were drawn up without delay. The members of the faculty would constitute "The Consulting Staff." An attending staff of six physicians, elected by the faculty but not members of it, would render necessary service at the Dispensary, daily except Sunday, from 1 to 3 P.M. The attending and consulting physicians would together form the Medical Board which would manage the institution. The faculty proceeded to elect the attending staff and appropriated $50 for medical supplies at once.[23]

CHAPTER EIGHT

Curriculum Reform

In the decade following the War of 1861-1865 so much attention was given to the problems of the physical accommodation of the school and its activities that little mention of the discussion of educational questions is found in the records. There is, however, evidence of new insistence upon the strict observance of rules and established procedures. For example, there was constant effort to require the purchase of tickets for courses *in advance,* and finally the dilatory (or impecunious) were not permitted to buy tickets for the *previous* course after October 1. Lack of a ticket would involve loss of credit for the course that had been taken. In 1877 the cost for the full course was fixed at $140 and that fact communicated to the Georgetown Medical faculty as a matter of reciprocity. The faculty resolved "that fair average attainment be made the indispensable prerequisite for examination." Tri-weekly, weekly, or occasional examinations throughout the regular sessions were made obligatory on all students for graduation.[1]

A further attempt was made to raise standards by improving examination procedures. The faculty was divided into two committees, each of which was to examine one student at a time. One, a committee of four, was to examine in the primary branches; the other, a committee of three, in the practical branches. Written examinations, in addition to the oral, were obligatory. A tremendous amount of time was expended on these oral examinations, sessions begun early in the evening often running until midnight.[2]

A change in curriculum of major significance was made by the faculty on July 11, 1897, when the following rule was adopted: "It shall be obligatory upon the candidates for graduation to attend three graded courses of lectures before their final examination" upon recommendation of a special committee. The same committee was directed to prepare the curriculum, dividing the courses into special branches to be studied each year. The changes were made immediately effective and published in the catalogue for 1879-1880. The major innovations were the three-year requirement and graded courses. These were set forth in the catalogue as follows:

Candidates for the Degree of Doctor of Medicine must have attended three courses of lectures, the subjects to be arranged as follows:

First Year: Anatomy, Physiology, Chemistry, and Materia Medica. Practical Anatomy and Histology.
Second Year: Anatomy, Physiology, Chemistry, and Materia Medica. Practice of Medicine, Surgery and Obstetrics, Histology, Practical Anatomy, Clinics. Examination at end of second year in Anatomy, Physiology, Chemistry, and Materia Medica.
Third Year: Practice of Medicine, Surgery, Obstetrics and Pathological Histology, Clinical Medicine, and Surgery. Final examination at end of this course.

Candidates for graduation must have studied medicine three years, or the term of three years' study must be completed at a date not exceeding three months after the period of the final examination. They must be of good moral character and at least twenty-one years of age.

The candidate shall have dissected at least two sessions, and have attended two courses of clinical instruction.

The entire expense for a Full Course of Lectures by all of the Professors is $135

Single Tickets	$20
Practical Anatomy by the Demonstrator	$10
Matriculating Fee, payable only once	$ 5
Graduating expenses	$30

The student is required to pay twice only for the ticket of each professor; succeeding attendance is free of expense.

The requirement of an inaugural thesis, written in the student's own handwriting on some medical subject, had been long on the books and was included in the new plan, but was shortly abolished.[3]

"The plan of instruction," said the catalogue, "adopted by this Institution comprises a complete course of scholastic lectures on the seven essential branches of medical science, viz.: Anatomy, Physiology, Materia Medica, Chemistry, Surgery, Obstetrics, and the Theory and Practice of Medicine, by which the student becomes thoroughly versed in the *principles* of his profession; and conjoined with this, ample opportunities will be afforded for bedside instruction by which the general principles taught in the lecture-room can be verified, illustrated, and *practically* applied, under the immediate observation of the student."

Emphasis was laid on visual aids in instruction, and on practical laboratory work assisted by the use of microscopes and necessary appliances. Providence Hospital, Columbia Hospital for Women, Children's Hospital, the Washington Asylum, and Freedmen's Hospital were listed as offering abundant opportunity for clinical instruction. The dissecting room, newly constructed and amply equipped, was open until 11 P.M. with a demonstrator of anatomy in charge.

It is evident that there were new hands, new energy, new thinking at work. Looking at the whole field of medical education at the time, it is apparent that Columbian's Medical College was reacting to the forces that were moving all of the medical schools of the time out of a dismal age into a period of marked progress. According to the Commissioner of Education's Report in 1870, only two colleges, one which became the Medical School of Northwestern University and the other the Women's Medical College of the New York Infirmary, had a graded course of lectures lasting three winter sessions, though Northwestern did not make this curriculum obligatory until some time later. The Harvard Medical School inaugurated its three-year graded course in 1871-1872. Columbian was not far behind.[4]

During the 'seventies, several important figures in the life of the National Medical College passed on, among them Dr. Thomas Miller (1806-1873), Dr. William P. Johnston (1811-1876), Dr. William B. Drinkard (1842-1877), and Dr. John C. Riley (1828-1879). Dr. Johnston, a graduate of Yale, with his degree in Medicine from Pennsylvania, was president of the Medical faculty for many years, professor of surgery, 1842-1845, and of obstetrics and the diseases of women and children, 1845-1871. He is said to have been the first physician in Washington to specialize on the diseases of women.[5]

William Beverly Drinkard, M.D. 1866, M.R.C.S., was a son of President Buchanan's Secretary of War. He studied medicine in Paris and assisted Desmarres in ophthalmology. Busey says that he was the first physician in the city who made ophthalmology his specialty. "He was great in every capacity of life, noble in every circumstance and act, and true and faithful in every relationship," wrote one among his many eulogists. From the year of his graduation until his death eleven years later he was progressively demonstrator, lecturer, and professor of anatomy.[6]

John Campbell Riley, M.D. 1851, was the son of Dr. Joshua Riley whom he succeeded in 1859 as professor of materia medica, therapeutics, and pharmacy. For a score of years he served as dean of the Medical faculty. In sustained labor, day by day, few men have contributed more to the Medical College than Dr. Riley. His colleagues

Resolved: That in reviewing his career of usefulness, both as Dean of the Faculty and as Professor of Materia Medica embracing a period of twenty years, we cannot but admire the fidelity and persevering industry which have so conspicuously characterized the performance of his various duties, even when labouring under the physical disability which must have warned him of his approaching end.[7]

CHAPTER NINE

Problems of Growth

The adoption of the curriculum reform of 1879 inaugurated the deanship of Dr. Albert Freeman Africanus King. Due in large measure to the personal dynamism of this gifted teacher and administrator, a period of marked activity got under way in every phase of the School's work. There was continuing effort to improve educational procedures, to enrich the curriculum, to strengthen the faculty, and to undertake new fields of professional training. Always present was the pressing need for more space and, perhaps more basically, for the necessary funds to provide for expansion.

There was a marked tendency toward detail in faculty legislation. If a student was formally failed on his examination, there had to be a lapse of six months before a reexamination could be taken. The whole examining process was laid out in detail. The first step was the written examination in two stages. First, those who had any of the preliminary branches to be examined in were to be given questions, prepared beforehand in writing, and designed to be completed for each branch within an hour. Second, those who had final branches to be examined in were given written questions, with one hour allowed for each branch. Papers did not bear the candidate's name but were designated by a special number, known only to the dean.

The second step was the oral examination. The orals could not be taken until the written papers had been handed in and read by the assigned examiner. Failure to appear forfeited the right to examination at that time, unless special arrangements had been made.

In grading a student the individual professor decided, for his field, the relative importance to be assigned to the written answers and to practical demonstrations. A much coveted examination prize was offered each year to the student making the highest total score on all examinations. In computing this score the maximum grade allowed for each branch, written and oral, was 10.

Although the thesis requirement was still included in the new rules (it was very quickly eliminated), tests of literary ability were applied at other points in the curriculum. Applicants for admission who could not offer a certificate from some college, high school, or seminary were examined by Professor Fristoe in English composition, mathematics, geography, history, etc. An examination in the English branches had to be passed. before an applicant was allowed to matriculate. Each student was required to dissect two parts of a subject at each of two sessions, or three parts at each session if material was provided.[1]

Registration had shown a tendency to average between 50 and 60 students. By 1881, the fee for a full course had reached $135. It was felt that this was something of a deterrent to registration when it was pointed out that of the 63 medical colleges in the country, only 18 charged more than $100 for a full course and some of those $105, with the remaining 45 charging less than $100. To improve Columbian's competitive position, the fee for the full course, beginning with the 1881-1882 session, was reduced to $100 and the cost of single tickets from $20 to $15.[2]

It would appear that the effect of the reduction of fees was almost magical. During the 1880's the number of students increased rapidly. By the end of the decade more than 100 were on the rolls; the 1891 catalogue shows 158 students. Other factors were no doubt operative, particularly the progressive improvement and enlargement of the School's quarters. Prosperity was also suggested in the very radical increase of the amount of the dividends declared. Up until the early 1880's, $200 had been a normal dividend, but in 1883 the dividend was $350; in 1884, $425; in 1885, $375; in 1886, $550; and in 1887, $600. An entirely new charge on the budget was incurred. Recognizing that the Office of Dean was no longer held in annual rotation but in what amounted to permanent tenure, and that the duties of the office had vastly increased, the dean in 1886 was voted a commission of 2½ per cent on the annual proceeds, in addition to such dividends as might accrue to him as a member of the faculty.[3]

In 1881, a graduate of Howard University was admitted to the Medical College, and in the following year the lecture courses of Howard were recognized as the equivalent of those of other institutions on the *ad eundem* list.[4]

Women had a more difficult time in gaining admission. It will be recalled that when an inquiry was made in 1855 on behalf of two women seeking admission, they were tersely informed that they would not be received. In 1872 the Board of Trustees refused to accept a proffered donation of a scholarship for a young woman in Columbian College. When the establishment of the University's Corcoran Scientific School was being discussed, the question of the admission of women came up again. The Trustees decided that no hard and fast rule should be set, but that each faculty should make the decision for its own school, subject to the Board's approval. This called for a statement of policy on behalf of the Medical faculty. The dean informed the Trustees that a majority of his faculty opposed the admission of women then, but would favor it as soon as proper accommodations could be provided.

In December, 1884, just four months later, four women—Ellen W. Cathcart, Sarah A. Schull, Alice J. White, and Mrs. Clara Bliss Hinds—petitioned for admission. The dean stated that the faculty would welcome them and admit them on the same basis as men. His explanatory letter is interesting:

Dean's Office, December 11, 1884. To the President and Board of Trustees of the Columbian University.

Gentlemen:

In accordance with the foregoing petition the medical faculty respectfully request authority from your Honorable Board for the admission of female students to the medical department on the same footing as males are now admitted.

Since it may appear to be somewhat wayward on the part of the faculty to have changed its decision on this matter since the last meeting of the Board of Trustees, it may be stated that the signers of the foregoing petition having, by permission of the faculty, attended the lectures this winter (but without matriculation or other official recognition) and having found that the inconvenience from the want of proper retiring rooms, (which the faculty had thought would be an obstacle to their attendance), is not in reality an insuperable difficulty, but one with which they (the ladies) are quite willing to put up—the objection on the part of the faculty to the admission of female students is withdrawn.

So far, the conduct of the male pupils toward the female ones, has been uniformly polite, as stated by the ladies themselves, and no objection on the part of the male pupils has been made to the admission of females.

Signed:

A. F. A. King, M.D., Dean
D. Webster Prentiss, Prof.
Mat. Med.
J. Ford Thompson, Prof. Surgery
Elliott Coues, Anat. Prof.
W. W. Johnston, Med. Theory
and Practice
E. T. Fristoe, Prof. Chemistry
William Lee, M.D., Prof.
Physiology

The approval of President Welling and the Board of Trustees was immediately forthcoming, but the last chapter in the story was yet to be written.[5] The central figure in the next chapter, oddly enough, was a member of the faculty and a graduate of the College and the Medical School.

Elliott Coues (1842-1899), A.B. 1861, A.M. 1862, M.D. 1863, Ph.D. 1869, was professor of anatomy from 1882-1887. While for the greater part of his active life he was an assistant surgeon, U.S.A., he long maintained a connection with the Smithsonian Institution, belonged to most of the scientific societies of the period, and found time to write prolifically on ornithology (perhaps his specialty), mammology, herpetology, comparative anatomy, theosophy, and psychic research. A lengthy tour of duty in Washington gave him an opportunity to teach. That a person of such wide-ranging interest and intellectual curiosity would interlard his lectures with a wealth of allusions not always germane to his subject might well be expected. It apparently worked out that way.

At a faculty meeting on March 21, 1887, Professor Fristoe pointed out that "the course of Lectures on Anatomy has been somewhat incomplete" and offered a resolution, unanimously adopted: "That the Professor of Anatomy be requested to confine his lectures, as far as possible to that subject." At the next faculty meeting, ten days later, Professor Coues called attention to the resolution and "after a pleasant exchange of views on the matter" expressed his willingness to comply.

The next item of business also concerned the professor of anatomy. The faculty had resolved to omit the customary publication of the Commencement Address for 1887. The speaker had been Dr. Coues and his subject "A Woman in the Case." The subject, certainly an arresting one for a Commencement speech, was suggested by the fact that among the graduates that year was Clara Bliss Hinds, one of the first group of women admitted to the Medical School and later the author of *Child Growth* and *Is Discrimination Against Women by Insurance Companies Wise?* Dr. Coues stated quite frankly that if the College did not publish his address, he would publish it at his own expense in book form. The faculty insisted that it must not be issued as an address delivered at the Commencement of the Medical Department of Columbian University. Every member present stated his reasons for this decision. Coues admitted that these were strong objections. No further action was taken, "but it was hoped Dr. Coues would so far consider the interests of the University as to desist from publishing the address, which he with some reluctance, partially consented to do." Very shortly Dr. Coues resigned his chair, but not before he carried out his intention. The booklet appeared with Brentano's imprint and with full reference to the occasion of the delivery of the speech.

Preceding the text is a long letter to the faculty. Saying that because he had been advised both to print and not to print, he had used his own judgment. He disclaimed any desire to hurt the University; and even though he might seem to, it was the University's mission to direct public opinion. He denied that any insult to true religion was intended or expressed. If there were any blame it was his alone, not the College's, and he offered to resign after expressing his best wishes for the success of the College and his abiding friendship for his colleagues. His offer to resign, needless to say, was accepted.

The address begins with the assertion that it had taken the Medical Department "more than three score years to grow wise enough to secure what was needed—a woman graduate." For four pages in lighthearted and amused banter, he described the efforts of women to be admitted to the Medical School. In colorful recital he traced the unequal role of women in human history. Why did it take so long for women to claim their own? The three great stumbling blocks were: religious intolerance, scientific insolence, and social tyranny.

It was his discussion of the first stumbling block that really drew blood. His assault on organized Christianity was vitriolic and tasteless. The Roman Church had "galvanized anew a creedal corpse, propped up on two legs which are the Devil and Damnation, backed up by the dogma of papal infallibility. . . . Henry VIII imposed upon the predominant race of men a placid and intensely respectable Episcopacy, that emasculate bastard of the scarlet woman of Rome."

"Scientific insolence," he said, "was that peculiar exhibition of vanity which men make when they act as if they thought masculine intellect superior to feminine intuition. . . . Social tyranny which involves us all but terrorizes women especially, is too pointed to need sharpening by any words of mine."

How long will this go on? "Only one thing is safe to say: Men never act alone. They cannot. They may think they do, but they do not. The only safe prediction is this: Whatever the case may be, there will be a woman in the case—God bless her!"[6]

The appearance of the name of Professor E. T. Fristoe (1827-1892) on the faculty list deserves some comment. Professor Fristoe was not a medical man but the professor of chemistry in Columbian College, a graduate of Virginia Military Institute with an M.A. from the University of Virginia and a degree in pharmacy. He taught in the College from 1855 to 1860 and in the University of Missouri, 1860-1862. After serving as a colonel in the Army of the Confederate States in command of a famous outfit known as Fristoe's Missouri Cavalry, he returned to the College in 1865 where he taught for the remainder of his life. In 1871 he began also to teach in the Medical College. A scientist and teacher of marked ability, he had great influence throughout the University and was actively involved in the educational policy of both the College and the Medical School. In addition to his teaching activities, Professor Fristoe administered the admissions requirements for the Medical College.[7]

For years, the short spring session was an important part of the School's activities. Always self-supporting, it offered no financial difficulties. Elastic in its program, it gave an opportunity for enrichment to the School's offerings without any permanent commitments to the instructors. It was not limited to "the historic septenary." The courses of lectures were on several levels. Some of them might properly serve as refresher courses, some of them were concerned with new drugs and new techniques designed to update the knowledge of men in active practice. In 1884, Dr. Kidder, U.S.N., was asked to lecture on "The Germ Theory of Disease." At times, the spring session offered an opportunity to bring in visiting lecturers of great eminence to discuss their specialties, for example, Dr. Theobold Smith lectured on bacteriology in the session of 1886. Other courses were offered on topics which would interest cultivated people generally. The great explorer and scientist, John Wesley Powell, lectured on "Primitive Medicine" in 1881. By faculty action, lecturers in the spring term were to be titled "Professors." Included among the spring lecturers when this action was originally taken was one young man who had not yet received his M.D. In one of the rare touches of humor in the *Dean's Book*, he is designated in quotation marks "Professor of Minor Surgery and Bandaging."

With the marked increase in the size of the student body and, consequently, of the graduating class, the annual Commencement had become quite a gala occasion. An effort on the part of President Welling to have the medical Commencements postponed until June, when the University Commencement was held, was successfully resisted by the Medical faculty.[8]

While the graduation program remained basically unchanged in details, much attention was given to its planning. A typical Commencement was the one held on the evening of March 17, 1881, in Lincoln Hall, at the corner of 9th and D Streets. We are told that

The stage was very elegantly decorated and presented a handsome appearance. The rear wall was tapestried with a large American flag, and at each side flags were tastefully draped. The words "National Medical College" glowed above in gleaming gas jets. Foliage plants lined the sides of the stage, and the front was a perfect bank of brightly colored flowers and plants. One floral tribute, representing a ladder made of white flowers, with a crown of white flowers suspended over the top and the steps made of red flowers, was especially noticeable.[9]

The students exceeded their available funds in this magnificent display, because two days later the faculty made an appropriation of $8 "to enable the students to complete the purchase of gas jets used in decorating the Hall for Commencement." Music at the 1881 Commencement, as at so many others, was provided by the Marine Band. "The xylophone solo received a hearty encore." Twelve students in formal evening attire served as ushers. The address, delivered by a member of the faculty each year in rotation, was given by Professor Fristoe. The usual press comments were passed upon it: "a scholarly production, complete with valuable suggestions and advice." The prayer was, as always, "fervent and impressive." The usual faculty supper, at which the professors served in rotation as hosts, was given in 1881 by Dr. A. F. A. King at "Aman's

Restaurant." Six years later, the size of graduating classes having out-
grown the limits of individual hospitality, it was ordained that the Commencement supper would be given by the entire faculty, presumably
at the expense of the general fund.[10] The cost that year for the dinner,
given at Solari's Restaurant, 1411-13 Pennsylvania Avenue, on Commencement evening was $1 per plate.[11]

From the earliest days of the occupancy of the H Street building
there had been frequent complaints about the lack of adequate space.
Many modifications had been made in the building—in fact, practically
everything possible short of major reconstruction. The steady growth
in the number of matriculants should mean good financial health. In
fact this was attested by the increasingly larger dividends voted to
themselves by the faculty. A more aggressive financial policy was evolving. In February of 1886, the dean reported the investment of $2,000
in government bonds which would produce some interest before the
close of the year. In the fall of the same year the advice of the faculty
was asked on the temporary investment of money during the winter
term. Like good businessmen they were evidently putting their operating surplus to work rather than let it lie fallow in a checking account.[12]

Desultory discussion of the founding of a dental department had now
entered upon an active phase and further underscored the need for more
space. A special committee to make positive recommendations was
appointed. Renewed pressure was exerted upon President Welling, urging the necessity of enlarging the building and of acquiring the stable
and lot adjacent to the School. Confident that positive action was in the
offing, the dean began to inventory all of the movable property in the
building to determine what belonged to the School and what to individuals.[13]

The question of funding the construction obviously offered problems.
As far as its proprietary status went, the School was in a transitional stage
in which some strange contradictions figured. The Medical College was
using a building which belonged to the University, on the basis of
which fact the Board of Trustees had expressed its intention to play a
larger part in the control of the Medical College. To bring about the
exemption of the building from taxation as being held by a nonprofit-
making organization, the Board had decreed that the Medical College
was an integral part of the institution and put the faculty on the basis of
salaried ($1 per year) officers of the University. At this time the Medi-
cal College was demanding an expensive piece of reconstruction on a

property owned by the institution. The medical staff offered the Board of Trustees an ingenious plan. The Trustees would get the cash for building by borrowing $10,000 secured by a mortgage on the property. The Medical faculty would consider this a loan at 5 per cent until the Trustees could pay off the principal and raise the mortgage.

The Trustees made a counterproposal which was accepted by the faculty, Mr. Corcoran's assent being given. The Board would borrow the money by a mortgage on the property. The Medical Department would pay annually 5 per cent interest and 2½ per cent to a sinking fund.[14] At the request of President Welling, the dean agreed in the future to send the president an annual report of the Medical Department, including all expenses and receipts, to be presented to the Board at its annual meeting in June of each year. The Trustees had not changed their policy.[15]

While financial negotiations were going on, Mr. W. B. Gray, an architect, had prepared preliminary plans for the improvements: extending the existing building to the rear and adding another story. The architect estimated that the cost would be something in excess of $11,000. His commission was to be 2½ per cent of cost, not including the cost of superintendence. When the plans and specifications were turned over to Mr. William C. Morrison, the builder, he fixed the cost roughly at $8,665.[16]

In addition to the work originally planned, at an added cost of $172 the builder converted the attic space under the new roof into a storage room with trap door and ventilating skylight. The committee on building was authorized to put in gas lights and whatever else was necessary when the contractors had finished their work. The financial agreement between the faculty and Trustees was implemented by the faculty's agreement to pay 5 per cent interest and $250 to the sinking fund each year until the whole sum was paid or arranged for by bequest or otherwise, when the entire amount paid into the sinking fund would be returned to the Medical faculty.[17]

While the building was being reconstructed the lectures of the Medical faculty were given in the University Building at 15th and H Streets. At the same time that arrangements were being made jointly by the Trustees and the Medical College to carry new indebtedness, attention was belatedly given to an old debt. Unpaid taxes on the College property for 1873, 1874, and 1875 amounted, with penalties, to about $2,000. Through the kind offices of President Welling, the Trustees loaned

$2,000 to the Medical faculty which, in turn, gave four notes for $500 each at 5 per cent. The payment of $1,939.46 to the District finally cleared up the amount owed before the School qualified as a nonprofit-making institution entitled to tax exemptions. In view of the fact that the tax exemption by the Commissioners had been brought about by a maneuver in which the Trustees solemnly declared that the Medical Department was an integral part of the University in verification of which the professors were paid annual salaries ($1) by the University, the method of financing the reconstruction of the Medical building was highly interesting. Especially was this so in light of the fact that the professors continued to vote themselves annual "dividends" in increasingly larger amounts until 1890, when the annual distribution of funds was referred to for the first time as a "salary." Whether this amount was in addition to the mythical $1 from the University is not stated. It is significant that the dean was now under instructions from President Welling to submit annual financial reports to the Trustees.[18]

The pressing need for more space in the Medical building had forced the discontinuance of various desirable activities. The faculty had announced its intention to maintain the Washington Ear and Eye Infirmary to afford clinical facilities and instruction to students in 1887, but after a few months had had to tell the professor in charge, Dr. Francis B. Loring, that room for this purpose was no longer available.[19] If there was no space for carrying on work to which they were already committed, certainly no new large project could be undertaken unless some major additions of space were acquired.

CHAPTER TEN

The Dental School

Thought had been given to the establishment of a College of Dentistry for several years. In fact, the matter had been formally considered in 1883 and a committee appointed to investigate and report. A year later after hearing from the committee, the faculty decided that the establishment of a Dental Department at the time was inadvisable. Curiously, though, the organization of a Veterinary Department was discussed at the same meeting. Interest in a Dental School continued. As plans for financing and constructing larger quarters got under way, plans for establishing a Dental School began to crystallize. In April of 1887, the Medical faculty voted to postpone the publication of the annual catalogue because of uncertainty as to the establishment of the Dental Department. Late that spring the Medical faculty had decided on nominations for the chairs in the proposed department: operative dentistry, Louis C. Hugo, D.D.S., with Dr. H. C. Thompson as alternate; prosthetic dentistry, Drs. R. B. Donaldson and J. Hall Lewis, conjointly.[1]

The opening of the Dental Department was formally approved by the governing board of the University on June 13, 1887. Dr. H. C. Thompson was confirmed as professor of operative dentistry, and Dr. J. Hall Lewis as professor of prosthetic dentistry. Ground rules for receiving the first group of matriculants had been laid down. Five years of dental practice was accepted, for purposes of the examination, as equivalent to one course of lectures. If a candidate passed at least three branches satisfactorily, he received credit for them without further examination. Students who, because of credit for previous dental practice, were examined at the end of one course of lectures would, if they were required to take a second course or part of such a course, pay for tickets to courses they were required to study a second time. However, in the case of failure of a student who had paid for a full course of lectures in Columbian and for a full course in another dental school, there would be no charge for further instruction. A matriculation examination would be required of all applicants in writing, spelling, grammar, composition, arithmetic, geography, and elementary history. Each dental student was required to dissect in one session; this would be sufficient, provided the dissection included a head and a neck. The dean, however, was given dispensing power for those for whom dissecting material was not provided. The new diploma plate was ordered to be in English, not Latin.[2]

On the recommendation of a joint committee a detailed set of regulations was adopted defining fiscal and other relations between the Medical and Dental faculties. The customary procedures of the Medical faculty determined the lines of the arrangement. Receipts and expenditures of the Dental Department were to be recorded in ledgers and cash-books separate from those of the Medical Department. The breakdown was clearly indicated. Dentistry was to be charged with "costs of dental chairs, lathes, spittoons, extracting forceps, and all other apparatus, instruments, and materials required in teaching dentistry and in operating the clinical dispensary service at the Dental Infirmary, together with all plates, diagrams, and other methods of instruction used in the lecture rooms, and the repair of same, also extra janitor's fees, and official advertisements of the Dental School, diplomas and the new dental plate" (for engraving the diplomas). The Dental Department was not to be charged with any part of the outlay incurred in the teaching of anatomy, physiology, chemistry, therapeutics, and oral surgery; or with any part of the running expenses of the College, such as fuel, gas, water, rent, fire insurance, catalogues (unless special dental circulars were issued), postage, general advertising, Commencement expenses, annual supper; or with ordinary repairs to the College building from general wear and tear.

The receipts of the Dental Department were to include matriculation and examination fees, and the fee for tickets for anatomy, physiology, chemistry, therapeutics, prosthetic dentistry, and operative dentistry paid for by the students of Dentistry. After each annual Commencement, the net profits of the Dental Department were to be divided into six equal shares, of which the professor of operative dentistry and the professor of prosthetic dentistry should each receive one share. The remaining four shares were to be turned over to the general fund of the Medical faculty, i.e., the seven professors constituting the faculty before the organization of the Dental Department.

The Dental Department was to contribute one-fourth of the annual expenditure of $750, i.e., 5 per cent interest on the loan for remodeling the building and 2½ per cent for the sinking fund.

No medical student could become a dental student or vice versa without having presented to the dean a written request for transfer; this was then to be automatically granted, all fees paid being credited to the school in which the student was then registered. A student could transfer only once during a single session. A dental student having passed his examination as such, was required after the transfer to stand reexamination in all the primary branches before the Medical faculty, since the medical examination required a knowledge of histology which the dental examination did not. Dr. A. F. A. King, the dean of the Medical Department, was to be dean ex officio of the Dental Department, but the two faculties were to meet separately when necessary. Ownership of all movable property of the Dental Department was to be vested in that department exclusively.[3]

These arrangements for the salary of the dental professors remained in force even after entirely new salary arrangements were made for the Medical faculty. When in 1897 the Trustees assumed formal possession of the Medical building with title to all equipment, furniture, and apparatus, and with it general management and control, the seven members of what then had become the executive committee of the Medical faculty were assigned a minimum salary of $1,000 a year each, with $500 additional to the dean, along with a division of the surplus. The old system of one-sixth of the net proceeds to each of the two professors of the Dental faculty, with payment of the remaining two-thirds to the general funds of the Medical School, was still retained. This action, however, was only a prelude to a more sweeping change effected shortly thereafter.[4]

CHAPTER ELEVEN

Educational Expansion and Administrative Change

The establishment of a Dental School was but one of many significant changes in the last decade and a half of the nineteenth century. Although the Medical faculty was busily engaged in working out the details of its relationship with the new Dental faculty, it found time to turn to a problem which had long caused concern. It had been felt that there was grave inadequacy in the work in histology as then being given. Instruction was henceforth to be given in the physiological laboratory. New equipment was bought and installed: three tables; five more microscopes; two rows of lockers, each a foot square, with twelve lockers in each row and one key for each row; two dozen stools. With this new laboratory equipment available, attendance was made obligatory, with all absences to be reported to the dean. For 1887-1888, the second-year class was scheduled for Tuesday and Saturday at 8:30; one half of the first-year class on Tuesday at 7:30 and the other half on Saturday at 7:30. For 1888-1889, the requirements were:

> First-year class, two hours a week in normal histology and microscopic histology;
> Second-year class, one hour a week review of normal histology and beginning pathological histology;
> Third-year class, two hours a week in pathological histology.[1]

Dental students were not admitted to the histological courses.[2]

The care with which histological study was introduced into the traditional curriculum shows a gratifying awareness of the need to keep up with advances in medical education. When at about the same time a member of the Medical faculty suggested the establishment of a nucleus of a medical library in conjunction with the general University Library for the use of medical students, the president of the University stated his support of the idea if it could be "so arranged as to prevent the younger boys of the University from obtaining access to books the perusal of which might be objected to by their parents"! Action on the suggestion was deferred.[3]

It might have been a touch of that same sense of Victorian delicacy which led to a reopening of the question of coeducation in medicine. In the spring of 1892, the faculty voted to discontinue the admission of women to the Medical School after seven years' trial. The Trustees' approval of the action was requested since "the interests of the medical department have rendered such a course necessary." The action would have been unanimous but for the opposing vote of Dr. William Lee, Professor of Physiology, who also refused to sign the memorial setting forth the reasons for the action taken; this was handed to President Welling. The president asked that the matter be presented to the governing body at its June meeting. Before this could be done the ladies presented a memorial arguing against the action of the faculty. To allow time for further thought the faculty voted to reconsider. The dean thanked the ladies for their memorial, saying that their arguments would be considered but a personal interview was not thought necessary.

A special meeting of the faculty, with the Dental faculty participating, was called for a week hence (April 30) to consider the question again. Neither the *Minutes* of the Board nor those of the faculty contain the text of either of the memorials.

It was probably not wholly coincidental that at the meeting of April 23, apparently the major item on the docket was the adoption of rules for the dissecting room. The rules required each medical student before his examination to have dissected two "parts" of a subject during his first session and two "parts" during his second session. A dental student was required to dissect a head and one other "part" or two heads before his examination in the primary branches. The dissecting room would be open daily from 9 A.M to 11 P.M., with the demonstrator in the room each forenoon from 11 to 12 and each night from 10 to 11, with an assistant demonstrator present from 2 to 3 and from 8 to 10 P.M. After taking out the tickets of the professor of anatomy and the demonstrator, students were to form classes of five each and hand in the names in each group. Any student who was unable to get into such a class could have his name put on a list and be notified when the subject was ready. If he did not appear when called, his name went to the bottom of the list. There were the usual injunctions about careful and unhurried work and the maintenance of cleanliness and orderliness in the dissecting room.

These regulations were law, when a week later the faculty met, decided that its proceedings be considered confidential, and by a vote of 5 to 2 reaffirmed its original action excluding women, except that those already registered would be permitted to complete the course. At its annual meeting in June, the Board approved the request of the Medical faculty as submitted, but with the further condition that it would cooperate in any effort to establish a women's medical college in Washington. In taking its action, the Board stated its hope for an attempted "solution of the problem on a basis of the separation of the sexes in all instruction and operations involving what the faculty deem a strain on modesty."

In July, 1892, there were conferences between Trustees and professors and a compromise was suggested to admit women for one more year. This compromise was proposed to the Medical faculty at a meeting which rejected the compromise as reviving an unpleasant matter and in no way helping the establishment of a women's medical college. So ended another but not the final chapter on the subject.[4]

The third and final phase came about without any dramatics. After several attempts had been made, the registration of women in the professional schools was again authorized in June, 1911. Twenty years after the practice had been discontinued, President Stockton reported the admission of a woman to the Medical School.[5]

As the Board and the faculty came to a hesitant decision on coeducation in the summer of 1892, some important changes in personnel were made. To succeed the late Professor Fristoe, Dr. Emil A. deSchweinitz was elected lecturer in chemistry and toxicology for the 1892-1893 session, thus beginning a distinguished service with the Medical College that lasted for the remainder of his life. Dr. Theobald Smith, who had lectured during the short summer courses, was elected professor of bacteriology and hygiene. The conduct of examinations for matriculation, one of the many functions previously discharged by Professor Fristoe, was assigned to Professor William Lee. The examinations were to be given in accordance with the regulations of the Association of American Medical Colleges.

The North Side of H Street, Between 13th and 14th Streets, After the Marvin
Renovation.

Theobald Smith (1859-1934), M.D., Professor of Bacteriology, 1886-1895.

Walter Reed (1851-1902), M.D., Professor of Bacteriology, 1893-1902.

Frederick Fuller Russell (1870-1960), M.D., Professor of Bacteriology and Pathology, 1909-1913.

The memory of these three distinguished men of science is perpetuated by the Smith–Reed–Russell Society, election to which recognizes outstanding records of achievement in the work of the third and fourth years.

William Fowke Ravenel Phillips, M.D., Dean of the Medical School, 1904-1909.

Emil Alexander deSchweinitz, M.D., Dean of the Medical School, 1897-1904.

William Cline Borden, M.D., Dean of the Medical School, 1909-1931.

Joseph Ford Thompson, M.D., Last President of the Medical Faculty, 1887-1898.

Nurses' Home, 13th and L Streets, 1913-1931.

Designation of University Hospital on H Street as General Hospital 75, World War I.

Roland Walton, D.D.S., Dean, 1909-1918.

Henry C. Thompson, D.D.S., President of the Dental Faculty, 1887-1898.

J. Hall Lewis, D.D.S., Dean of the Dental School, 1894-1909.

Mary Winifred Glasscock, R.N., Superintendent of Nurses and Principal of the Training School, 1913-1918.

Two years after the Hospital and Medical School on the site of the original Corcoran building were completed, the name of the University was changed. The monogram CU on the lintel posts of the stairs remained a constant reminder until 1973—as long as the building was occupied—that George Washington University had once been Columbian University.

Medical School on H Street, Library.

Medical School on H Street, Hall A.

Biochemistry

Pathology

Anatomy

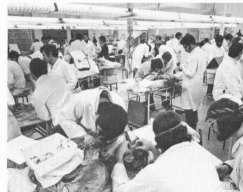

Gross Anatomy

Medical School on H Street, Laboratories.

A disposition to tighten requirements all around was evident. After pondering the question for months, a very radical change was made. The medical course was extended from three to four years' requirement for the degree. The time-honored custom of taking out a ticket for the lectures of each chair was discontinued, except when the lectures of a single chair were taken and a single ticket would be obtained for $20. For each of the four years there was an inclusive fee of $75 for all lectures and the examination. This fee, however, did not include the fees for matriculation and laboratory work, or for the demonstrator of anatomy. The fee was shortly increased to $100, with a matriculation fee of $25.[6]

There was evidence on every side of a determination to improve academic standards and of renewed emphasis on work in the laboratories and dissecting rooms, where time was now spent on rigid schedules, rather than on the basis of voluntary interest. Appropriations for laboratory equipment and material, though still modest, were larger and more frequent. The attention given to the organization of the work in histology has been noted. This was duplicated in other branches. When Dr. deSchweinitz came in, each student was charged a laboratory fee of $5, with a breakage fee of $5. Sections were limited to 16 and attendance was strictly enforced. A room in the rear of the building was assigned to Dr. deSchweinitz as a laboratory for research in biochemistry. Consideration was also given to setting up other specialized laboratories.[7]

It is interesting to note the value that the faculty placed on their plant. The apparatus and furniture were insured for $3,000, and the building for enough more to make a total coverage of $20,000. The maintenance staff was not large, as the following extract from the *Minutes* shows:

Dr. deSchweinitz moved that William Alexander [colored] be appointed an additional janitor to the Medical College at $15 per month for seven months of the session, and for the Dental Department at $5 per month for nine months: he is to stay in the College day and night, to sleep in the little front room under the stairway, supply his own bedding, and attend to the Dental Department, the electric lights, and to the histological, chemical, and bacteriological laboratories, while Daniel Conner—the old janitor—is to attend to the anatomical department, the furnaces, clean the lecture rooms, professors' rooms, and passageways (by scrubbing floors once a month) and ring the lecture bell, for which he is to receive $30 a month, for seven months of sessions from the Medical Department.[8]

The time during which the janitors were paid was shortly extended to cover the period from May 1 to October 1, when William Alexander was to get $15 per month and Daniel Conner $5 per month. Apparently "the little front room under the stairway" was lacking in heat, for in January, 1895, $2.25 was appropriated for a stove for Alexander.[9]

No sooner had the reconstruction and enlargement of the building been completed in 1888, than the need for still more space was felt. The next year the stables to the rear of the College lot were joined to the College. A faculty water closet was built in the stables and new plumbing was put in the two students' closets by way of tanks and ventilators. By 1892, the need for greatly increased space seemed so urgent that thought was given to borrowing a second $10,000 to reconstruct the building and establish laboratories. Plans were prepared by the Hornblower firm and shown to the Board of Trustees in the hope that the $20,000 that now appeared would be necessary would be available. The Board's reaction to a loan of $20,000 was not favorable, but it did offer $5,000 at 6 per cent to be amortized at the rate of $500 annually, paid into a sinking fund. Professor Francis R. Fava, Jr., of the Department of Civil Engineering had prepared plans and specifications for the proposed laboratories and other interior improvements, among them electric lighting, a furnace, and chairs for the upper lecture room. By the elimination of a furnace in the stable building, these changes were brought within the funds available and they were authorized.[10]

An innovation is noted in the official account[11] of the 1892 Commencement, held in Albaugh's Grand Opera House:[12] "N.B. The graduates wore caps and gowns for the first time." Whether this was the first time is open to some question. In the earliest Commencements in the 1820's, graduates were required to wear black silk gowns. Certainly this earlier practice had been long forgotten, when the wearing of the present type of academic costume was begun in the 1890's.

This adoption of traditional academic attire was thoroughly in accord with President Welling's desire to emphasize "the University Idea." To see this concept of higher education realized was perhaps his most cherished ambition. By amendment of the charter in 1873, Columbian College had become Columbian University. President Welling wanted to see the institution a university in function as well as in name. Basically his hope was that each department offering work on an undergraduate or professional level would extend its offerings to a postgraduate level, providing both courses of an advanced nature and programs of research. A series of new graduate schools would supervise these research projects and the courses supporting them and present candidates for higher degrees, including the doctorate. Welling realized that this would cost money, a great deal of money; but basic in his plan was the full utilization of the great resources of the government in the form of libraries, laboratories, and research facilities in general. Thanks to the availability of government experts in every field and of the government's facilities, insured by the joint resolution of Congress approved April 12, 1892, a dollar spent on higher studies in Washington would go further than a like sum spent anywhere else in the United States. President Welling laid out his plan in considerable detail and discussed it earnestly and persuasively with his Board and each of the faculties.

The language of the joint resolution could not have been better drawn to facilitate the type of cooperation that Welling had in mind:

Resolved by the Senate and House of Representatives of the United States of America in Congress assembled, That the facilities for research and illustration in the following and any other governmental collections now existing or hereafter to be established in the city of Washington for the promotion of knowledge shall be accessible, under such rules and restrictions as the officers in charge of each collection may prescribe, subject to such authority as is now or may hereafter be permitted by law, to the scientific investigators and to students of any institutions of higher education now incorporated or hereafter to be incorporated under the laws of Congress or of the District of Columbia, to wit:

1. Of the Library of Congress.
2. Of the National Museum.
3. Of the Patent Office.
4. Of the Bureau of Education.
5. Of the Bureau of Ethnology.
6. Of the Army Medical Museum.
7. Of the Department of Agriculture.
8. Of the Fish Commission.
9. Of the Botanic Gardens.
10. Of the Coast and Geodetic Survey.
11. Of the Geological Survey.
12. Of the Naval Observatory.[13]

In the winter of 1893, President Welling called a meeting of the faculty of the Medical Department to ask them to consider the organization of postgraduate instruction in the University. What he had in mind was original scientific investigation leading to the degree of Doctor of Philosophy. To attain this distinction, a knowledge of French and German had to be demonstrated before admission to candidacy, and a thesis would have to be written and defended. The president wanted to know if any of the professors of medicine would participate. The faculty had to say that they could do nothing because of lack of sufficient laboratory facilities. In spite of his meager resources, Welling took up the challenge. He offered a loan of $15,000 at 5 per cent from the University. When the faculty got their plans drawn up and specifications written providing for the structural and interior changes desired, and it was quite evident that funds much greater than the $15,000 would be necessary, the faculty settled on a much less ambitious program of interior modification.[14]

From a certain standpoint, the year 1894 was a significant one in the history of the Medical faculty. On May 1, 1894, Dr. A. F. A. King submitted his resignation as dean, the resignation to be effective as soon as the accounts for the 1893-1894 session could be closed and audited. His letter was typical of the man. He wasted few words in expressing regret at terminating a deanship that had lasted since 1879. He was much more concerned with the progress that had been made: registration tripled; finances improved through "the earnest and conscientious labors of its teachers"; standards raised through refusal to adopt "questionable methods" of getting students; "strict administration of admission and graduation requirements" more perhaps in obedience to principle than profit; satisfactory adjustment of the "woman question"; "the four-year system" weathered; indebtedness conscientiously reduced; relations with local hospitals satisfactorily developed; helpful stimulus furnished by the new and younger members of the faculty. It was a formidable list that would justify any man's pride.

Dr. King's determination to resign the deanship could not be shaken by the persuasion of his colleagues. With lavish protestations of regret, with assurances of deep appreciation, and with the warmest expressions of friendship, the resignation was accepted, and Dr. King made "Dean Emeritus." A formidable monument to the thoroughness and dedication of this gifted administrator is his record of fifteen years as dean in the *Dean's Books*, Vols. 1 and 2. Taking up 250 pages and written in his clear, bold hand is the concise, meticulous account of the official proceedings of a decade and a half. An indirect but nonetheless convincing testimony to his industry and versatility was the action taken at the time in which the duties that Dean King had performed were divided between a dean and a secretary-treasurer. Dr. D. F. Shute was elected dean, and Dr. Emil A. deSchweinitz secretary-treasurer.[15]

Four months after the change in the deanship James Clarke Welling, sixth president of the University, died. Welling became president in 1871, King became dean in 1879. In a period when the University was slowly but definitely extending its control over the Medical Department, there could have easily developed tensions of a most damaging character. Fortunately channels of communication between the president and the dean were always kept open, and the Medical faculty developed a high regard for the president. When shortly before his death Dr. Welling became seriously ill and then seemed to improve, the Medical faculty sent him cordial messages of encouragement. At his death the faculty formally recalled, with gratitude, "the energy, industry, and zeal with which he strove so persistently and continuously to promote the interests and progress of the Medical and Dental Schools." With the citizens of Washington and the members of the University, the faculty extolled those qualities of heart and mind "which have caused Dr. Welling to be so conspicuously honored, admired, and beloved by his companions and associates; honored as a man, admired as a scholar, and beloved as a friend."[16]

President Welling was succeeded by the Reverend Benaiah Longley Whitman, previously the president of Colby College.

Dr. King's successor as dean was Daniel Kerfoot Shute, A.B. 1879, M.D. 1883. He was the son of the Reverend Samuel Moore Shute, a member of the College faculty from 1859 to 1880. Dr. Shute's wife was the former Augusta M. Pettigrew, M.D. 1891. The new dean had been a clinical assistant in the Royal London Ophthalmic Hospital.

Welcome evidence of a desire for cooperation with other branches of the University began to appear. The Corcoran Scientific School, all of whose classes were given late in the day, was asked to include in its offerings a course preparatory to the study of medicine. Graduates of the Corcoran Scientific School with work in chemistry were to be given credit in the medical course for work already done.[17]

The troublesome problem of obtaining anatomical material was simplified and regularized by the Act for the Promotion of Anatomical and Surgical Science. At the request of the Health Officer of the District of Columbia, the demonstrator of anatomy was authorized as the representative of the faculty to receive bodies.[18]

Dr. Walter Reed was the speaker at the 1895 Commencement. At the time Dr. Reed was invited to be the speaker, it was known that Dr. Theobald Smith was planning to retire from the chair of bacteriology and pathology at the end of the current session. Professor Smith's resignation was accepted and Dr. Reed was elected professor of pathology and bacteriology. A course consisting of didactic lectures and laboratory instruction in pathology, pathological histology, and bacteriology was placed in the curriculum for the third year.[19] Six hundred dollars was borrowed from the University to be used in equipping a laboratory for bacteriology and pathology, and Drs. James Carroll and William S. Washburn were appointed Dr. Reed's assistants in bacteriology and in pathology and normal pathology, respectively.[20]

The question of beneficiaries had been a perennial cause of difficulty and embarrassment during the entire history of the College, and, after considerable effort, had been brought under fair regulation. It had never seemed quite possible to eliminate beneficiaries entirely. There was always a missionary, a son of a colleague, or the victim of some misfortune who was a basis for exception, creating no precedent, which, of course, it always did. When Mr. W. W. Corcoran made his gift of a building for use by the Medical College, it was felt proper that a limited number of scholarships be established in his honor. Inasmuch as the dividend paid the faculty was the proceeds from fees paid for student tickets, this represented an actual, although indirect, faculty expenditure. As long as W. W. Corcoran lived, nominations for scholarships came from him or from his representatives and were approved by him.

Following the death of Mr. Corcoran, the six Corcoran Scholarships were awarded on the basis of standing in a competitive examination. Two were reserved for the graduates of high schools in the District of Columbia; two were open to graduates of any reputable high school or college; two were open to those who were not graduates of any high school or college, but who gave evidence of fitness for the study of medicine. Evidence of pecuniary need, good morals, and industry were required of candidates in the last two categories.[21] A year later, on its own initiative, the faculty established two medical missionary scholarships.[22]

In June of 1895, what might be called a man-bites-dog incident occurred. The Medical Department had been a perennial applicant to the University for loans. We now have the reverse: the University had been seeking a president to succeed Dr. Welling, and the Reverend Benaiah L. Whitman was the choice. The Reverend Samuel H. Greene, who was serving as acting president in the interim, appeared before the Medical faculty, accompanied by the secretary-treasurer, Mr. Robert H. Martin. Dr. Greene made the preliminary statement. The election of Dr. Whitman was conditioned on the raising of a guarantee fund of $75,000 by the friends of the University in Washington, to be spent at the rate of $15,000 a year, for strengthening the Academic Department. Greene felt that Whitman could secure an adequate agreement in a few years which would strengthen all departments of the institution. He asked the moral support of the faculty.

Mr. Martin, at that time a figure of central importance in the University, then took over.[23] He called attention to the fact that the faculty had borrowed $10,000 from the University for use in improving and enlarging their building. If, said Martin, the University raised the $75,000 guarantee fund, it would cancel the debt. To help realize the guarantee fund, he asked that the Medical Department subscribe $500 a year for five years toward the fund, and that this be done in time so that an announcement of this subscription would have its major impact at a special meeting of the Alumni Association. The faculty made the subscription.[24]

No sooner had the faculty indulged in this act of benevolence than it became involved in a lengthy and significant controversy. In preparation for the session of 1895-1896, the chairman of the faculty committee on clinical teaching recommended that a schedule be given each student, with an individual notice to each member of the third and fourth classes stating which clinics and at what hours he should attend. Attendance at the time and place indicated was absolutely obligatory. Such a rigid schedule, obviously binding the professor as well as the student, gave no room for variation or for personal choice. Quite understandably it was resented by some clinical professors. They were set straight by the reminder that it must be understood that clinical professors and lecturers had no vote in the affairs of the College, that all matters would be decided by the regular faculty as customary. This rigid position, however, was modified by the assurance that clinical and special professors would be invited to meet with the regular professors for discussion twice each year, and that each of these would be given one-tenth of a vote on the merits of each student for examination. But they could not be given the right to sign diplomas as they had requested. Such an authorization was not within the power of the faculty.

When the regular and auxiliary faculties met for the first time, the auxiliary faculty had their demands formulated for explicit approval. Their petition that attendance at clinics be made compulsory and that they be given a fraction of a vote on examination was formally granted, as was the request that they have a voice in preparing the catalogue, that their names be printed along with those of the regular faculty and not in a separate listing, and that they be given the privilege of regular meetings with the faculty for educational discussion. Their request to sign diplomas was again denied. The dean read letters from the deans of Harvard, Yale, Pennsylvania, and the University of the City of New York, in all of which the professors of the seven essential branches formed the governing board. The conclusion of the faculty's deliberations lacked nothing in directness of statement: "This Medical faculty decided it would not surrender any of its rights as a governing body; but that it would continue then as heretofore."[25]

For some time the question of union with the National Veterinary College had been under consideration. In 1893, it was proposed to incorporate the Veterinary College as a new department of Columbian University, but the matter was dropped because the College did not want to become a part of Columbian University.[26] In March, 1896, the Board of Trustees voted to accept the faculty and curriculum of the Veterinary College, providing that it would in no way be a charge on the University, that its relationship would be like that of the Law and Medical Departments. Organized in 1892 as the National Veterinary College and affiliated with the University four years later, it was discontinued in 1898, except for some postgraduate work. It was reorganized as an affiliated college in 1908 and again discontinued in 1918.[27]

In the spring of 1897, Dr. Walter Reed asked to resign, pleading that his duties at the Museum left him no time for his work at the Medical College. He was asked to withhold his resignation. At the same meeting Dr. Shute offered his resignation, which was accepted with genuine regret. At the time of his election the office of secretary-treasurer of the faculty had been created to handle some of the increasing details of administration. That office was now discontinued and all of its functions were returned to the dean's office. Dr. Emil deSchweinitz was elected dean.[28]

CHAPTER TWELVE

New Construction;
The New Hospital

The highly significant changes and particularly the expansion of physical facilities that occurred at the turn of the century were in large measure the achievement of the young scientist who was called to the deanship in 1897. Emil Alexander deSchweinitz (1864-1904) was to serve the Medical School as dean during a very important period in its development. He was a member of a famed Moravian family, distinguished equally for its piety and its learning. After early training in Moravian schools in Pennsylvania, he was graduated from the University of North Carolina at the age of eighteen. Graduate work in chemistry and mineralogy followed at the University of Virginia, with the completion of his studies for the doctorate at the University of North Carolina in 1884. In the following year he went abroad for postdoctoral study at Berlin and Gottingen, receiving his second doctorate in philosophy at Gottingen in 1886. After a brief period of college teaching, Dr. deSchweinitz came to Washington as a chemist in the Department of Agriculture. He retained his connection with the Department for the remainder of his life, and at the time of his death he was chief of the Biochemic Division of the Bureau of Animal Industry. He came to the University, succeeding Dr. Fristoe as professor of chemistry and toxicology in the Medical School, and on the resignation of Dr. Shute was elected dean.

No sooner was Dr. deSchweinitz elected than he was involved in major plans for construction which were to continue in one way or another throughout his term of office. The closing of Columbian Academy afforded the opportunity for getting the first project under way.[1]

In 1882, the University, already determined to move all of its units to the center of the city, built a new and commodious home for the Preparatory School, shortly thereafter to be called the Columbian Academy, on the north side of H Street east of 14th Street. As the public secondary schools of Washington and Georgetown developed over a period of time, the need for private secondary schools was greatly reduced. The Columbian Academy was discontinued, and its building was now available for other University use. In the spring of 1897, the Board of Trustees had declared that if the Academy could be discontinued, the building could be used for a hospital.

Getting busy at once, a faculty committee estimated that if a new story were added, the necessary improvements would cost $10,000. If the present rooms were utilized, with a lift, the cost would be $6,000; with beds, apparatus, utensils, and other necessary items, an additional $2,000 would be required. Running expenses, assuming that all beds were occupied and there was a full force of servants, nurses, and doctors, were estimated at $600 per month. Faculty opinion, however, was mixed. Some thought it unwise to start without an endowment fund. Others favored beginning modestly with a Dispensary. The faculty considered asking the Trustees for $6,000. In a couple of days after this discussion they met with the Reverend Dr. Greene and Mr. S. W. Woodward, the merchant, both of them University Trustees. The Trustees listened sympathetically, and expressed interest and great appreciation of what the Medical faculty had accomplished with its own resources. They could naturally make no promises, but they wanted plans, specifications, and estimates.

It was evident what was in the offing. Another step was about to be taken in increasing the control of the Trustees over the Medical Department. As conferences went on between the Trustees' committee and the committee of the Medical and Dental faculties, points of agreement as reached were embodied in memoranda. The fourteen memoranda formed the basis for the plan of agreement that was adopted. The agreement was accepted by the Medical and Dental faculties on November 23, 1897, and by the Board of Trustees on December 18, 1897. The Hospital and General Dispensary would go into the old Preparatory School. The University assumed "immediate control" over the Medical and Dental Departments. The way it was done was shown in the memoranda, which in abridged form provided that:

1. The possession of the Medical Building was turned over to Columbian University.

2. Title to all furniture, fixtures, apparatus, and personal property of every description then belonging to the faculty as a body and used in connection with medical and dental instruction was vested in the University.

3. General management and control of the Medical and Dental Departments were vested in Columbian University as in the case of the other schools, only medical and dental appointments were to be by nomination by their respective Executive Faculty Committees. Executive Committees were to determine entrance qualifications. Women were not to be admitted except on recommendation of the faculty. Contracts with suppliers and clinical help were to remain in force and be assumed by the University.

4. The University assumed all debts of the Medical and Dental faculties.

5. Buildings and all appurtenances were to be used by the Medical and Dental Departments until the University provided "newer or better."

6. [The] present dean and faculty of the Medical and Dental Departments were continued, with appointments as in other schools.

7. The Executive Faculty of Medicine was to consist of the president and seven professors: Surgery, Theory and Practice of Medicine, Obstetrics, Materia Medica and Therapeutics, Physiology, Chemistry and Toxicology, and Anatomy. The Executive Faculty of Dentistry was to consist of the president and professors of Operative Dentistry, Prosthetic Dentistry, Materia Medica, Anatomy, Physiology, and Chemistry. Salaries of each were to be $1,000 per year, paid semi-annually, with an extra $500 to Dean deSchweinitz. Provided income exceeded total expenses including salaries, $1,000 was to be paid to the Hospital at the end of the year, and the surplus was to be divided, but only for a five-year period. If the University finances did not permit regular salaries to be paid, this arrangement was to be continued after the five-year period. Salaries of those not members of the Executive Faculty were to be fixed by the Executive Faculty and the University.

8. Financial arrangements with the Dental Department were to stand, but the $125 payment on the improvement loan was no longer to be made.

9. New equipment was to be paid for out of the revenue of the Department, but requisitions must not exceed income.

10. Faculties were to control growth and development of courses and fix hours.

11. Tuition received by the dean was to be paid to the University treasurer.

12. The agreement between the Medical and Veterinary Colleges was to remain in full force.

13. The University, with full cooperation of the Medical faculty, agreed to organize, establish, and equip a hospital and dispensary in the building of the former Preparatory School within one year from date.

14. Faculties would direct distribution of catalogues and placing of advertisements.[2]

On April 13, 1898, the Board of Trustees adopted an ordinance for the Hospital "for purposes of providing clinical instruction for students." It was to be maintained by fees, donations, and $1,000 annually from the receipts of the Medical School. The Hospital was opened November 1, 1898.[3] The Board of Governors of the Hospital consisted of the members of the executive committee of the Board of Trustees, and the executive faculty of the Medical School.

The former Preparatory School building, now transformed into a hospital, was a structure with three stories and a usable basement. On the first floor was a reception room for patients, offices, a waiting room, dispensary, and a special room for diseases of the eye, ear, nose, and throat. At the rear of the first floor a lobby led to the dispensary and pharmacy and adjoining these a dining room, with pantry, for the use of the hospital staff. An elevator shaft extended from the basement to the top floor.

On the second floor were two wards, one for men and one for women, the ward kitchen, and necessary bath and toilet rooms. The bathrooms were fitted with rolling tubs that could be taken to the bedside of the patient. On the top floor were several private rooms for patients, and rooms for nurses and the house doctor. On this floor was the amphitheater, with a properly equipped operating space. The roof had been raised somewhat to increase the height of the amphitheater. In the basement were the kitchen, the laundry, sleeping quarters for servants, and the heating apparatus. The Columbian Women, a society then newly organized, with a group of women students but recently admitted to Columbian College as a nucleus, took over a large part of the task of furnishing the rooms.[4]

Even more significant than the very considerable aid given by the Columbian Women in this initial phase of the Hospital's history was the assistance then begun and continuously maintained by the Board of Lady Managers of the Hospital. In addition to many other acts of thoughtfulness, these two groups of dedicated women, the first under the presidency of Mrs. C. W. Richardson and the second under the presidency of Mrs. William H. Hoeke, obligated themselves in a substantial way financially. The Columbian Women undertook to raise a fund for equipment, the Lady Managers to raise an annual sustaining fund of $2,500 for the maintenance of the Hospital.

Authorized under the ordinances for the Hospital on April 13, 1898, and formally organized a month later, the Lady Managers were able to present to the Hospital's Board of Governors at the end of their first year a report revealing an amazing achievement for so limited a period. It showed the thoughtfulness, the warm human sympathy, and the remarkable ingenuity which have characterized their fruitful activity through the years.[5]

Early in the spring of 1898, the organization of the staff of the Hospital got under way. It was decided that members of the staff working under the executive faculty would be called associates. In mid-July the staff was elected: for the Hospital, Dr. J. Ford Thompson in charge of surgery; Dr. William W. Johnston, medicine; and Dr. A. F. A. King, obstetrics and gynecology; for the Dispensary, Dr. C. W. Richardson, in charge of laryngology; Dr. T. R. Stone, genito-urinary; Dr. A. R. Shands, orthopedic surgery; Dr. D. W. Prentiss, nervous diseases; Dr. D. K. Shute, ophthalmology; Dr. G. Byrd Harrison, pediatrics; Dr. Emil deSchweinitz, clinical laboratory; Dr. Walter Reed, pathologist.

Two members of the Board of Lady Managers were added to the Board of Governors, as was Miss A. Gertrude Odell, the superintendent of the Hospital.

On the financial side pay patients could be kept in the wards at $5 to $7 a week. Dispensary doctors were to be informed that they must write inexpensive prescriptions. The duties of externs were defined as writing case histories, etherizing patients, "and other general work." A committee was appointed to join with a like committee from Georgetown to try to secure legislation through the District Commissioners providing for payment for charity patients in the Hospital.[6]

Meeting the need for a hospital had created a situation that involved a radical change in the relations of the Medical Department and the University. The Medical College now occupied two major University buildings. Because of the proprietary position of the faculty, the occupation of the first of these had created a tax problem which was resolved by declaring that the Medical College was an integral part of Columbian University, in evidence of which faculty members became salaried employees at a salary of $1 per year. The occupation of the second building, the old Prep, had brought about far more sweeping evidences of University control. The Medical College building and all of its appurtenances were declared the property of the University, and the financial hold of the faculty was liquidated. At the same time, real salaries rather than the fictitious $1 were voted: $1,000 dollars to each of the executive faculty, "the historic septenary," with an additional $500 to the dean.

Inasmuch as financial matters were so largely concerned with the readjustment of the University–faculty relationship, the annual report of the

President, presented to the Trustees and Overseers on June 1, 1898, gave a more than usual amount of statistical information. In the post-Civil War period, with but a few setbacks, there was a constant increase in the size of the student body. During the 'sixties, the enrollment varied from 17 to 70; during the 'seventies, from 44 to 56; during the 'eighties, from 44 to 128; and during the 'nineties to the time of the report, from 158 to 210. As to the realism of the salary of $1,000, no dividends were paid in the 'sixties, but beginning with $100 in 1870-1871, the dividends showed a fair relation to the size of the student body. It was not, however, until 1896-1897 that the dividend exceeded $1,000. For that year, it was reported as $1,017.00.

To indicate what the faculty had put into the property, the report stated that from 1871 to 1897, it had expended on the building, excluding running expenses, $33,956.58; on apparatus, $8,686.47; and for interest and payment on notes, $10,376. The faculty was therefore turning over an investment of more than $42,000 that they had made in the property, in addition to $10,000 repayment and interest on loans. More than ever, the Medical College was now an integral part of the University.[7]

In the detailed negotiations between the Board and the Medical faculty resulting in the memoranda of agreement that had defined their relationship, due care had been taken to recognize the interest of the newly established Dental Department and to maintain the basic arrangements between the Medical and Dental Departments fixed in 1887. Due to the interlocking of membership on the executive committees of the two departments, communication was open and natural.

On December 27, 1887, at the first meeting of the Dental faculty held separate from the Medical faculty, formal organization of the new department was effected. There were present: Professors H. C. Thompson, J. Hall Lewis, Fristoe, Lee, Prentiss, Shute, and King, ex officio, dean. Dr. A. F. A. King, who as dean of the Medical College had been the convener, was elected dean, without the right to vote but with the privilege of participating in the discussion of business. Dr. H. C. Thompson was elected president of the faculty and Dr. J. Hall Lewis was appointed curator of the properties of the Dental Department. Dr. Lewis was also placed in charge of the Dental Infirmary with authority to arrange with the demonstrator and the assistant demonstrators as to the order and time of their attendance, and to formulate rules for the regulation of students and patients during their attendance upon and participation in the clinical work of the Infirmary. The question of disposing of anticipated profits, brought up perhaps prematurely, was postponed to a later meeting.[8]

Candidates for admission were required to be conversant with the English language and to give evidence of having received a good elementary education either by a certificate of graduation or by examination. The original requirements for graduation were attendance upon two full courses, a final examination, and the preparation and presentation to the Museum of a practical specimen of the student's own dental handiwork. In 1889, the graduation requirement was increased from two to three years. Lectures commenced on the first Monday in October and continued through February. The length of the course was extended from time to time so as to be identical with that of the Medical Department. Fees were fixed as follows: matriculation, $5; full course of lectures each year, $90; single tickets $15; demonstrator of anatomy, $10; examination, $30. Rules similar to those of the Medical Department were adopted to allow transfer from dentistry to medicine or vice versa. Those transferring from other institutions were required to furnish a statement of good standing in the school previously attended, as well as an official statement of courses taken.[9]

A salary of $35 was voted each chair in 1890, $100 in 1891, and $180 in 1892. As in the Medical Department, 2½ per cent of the gross was paid, in addition, to the dean. Annoyance was expressed at people of ample means who were not deserving of free service but who nevertheless were abusing the Infirmary's charity service. A committee was appointed to investigate, but there is no record that a solution for the problem was found.[10]

On May 6, 1894, Dr. A. F. A. King resigned as dean of the Dental School. The faculty's expressions of regret were marked by great sincerity and depth of appreciation for the man who had added to his already arduous duties as dean of the Medical Department, very special problems as dean of the new Dental Department.

Dr. J. Hall Lewis was elected dean and Dr. H. C. Thompson reelected president of the faculty and its delegate to the National Association of Dental Faculties. Dr. Emil deSchweinitz was elected secretary-treasurer of the Dental Department.[11]

After reporting with considerable satisfaction that necessary improvements including new chairs and fixtures had been completed at the moderate cost of $600, the dean of the Dental School stated that the only jarring note in the very pleasant and friendly relations between faculty and students was resentment over the so-called "extra fees." The objection was met in a way that did not jeopardize the financial security of the School. All extra fees were abolished, but the fee for a full course was raised from $90 to $100, $25 of which had to be paid before a student would be admitted to laboratory or infirmary instruction. Three years later a graduation fee of $10 was added.[12]

Recalling that one of the compelling reasons for the enlargement of the Medical School building a quarter century before was the desire to provide accommodation for a Dental Department, it is interesting to note that in 1901 the Dental faculty instructed their dean to write to the Trustees and to call on the president to explain the serious problems that would arise when they were compelled to establish day instruction, and to point out emphatically that "this poor building and inadequate equipment made competition with neighboring dental schools impossible."[13]

Other voices had been heard. There had been constant suggestions made in the faculty that ground to permit expansion should be acquired. In the late fall of 1897, the Trustees had purchased the Widdicombe property on H Street between the Prep building and the Medical School, fronting 100 feet on H Street with a depth of 145 feet, at a cost of $90,000. A year had not yet passed before the Hospital was opened in the remodeled Prep building on November 1, 1898. But a few months later Dean deSchweinitz and Dr. J. Hall Lewis on behalf of the Medical and Dental faculties proposed to the Trustees the building of a new medical building on the old site. The matter was referred to a committee. When some considerable time had elapsed, President Whitman was asked at a faculty meeting what the prospects were for a new hospital and college building. He said he did not know, but would "pursue it at the next Board meeting." Perhaps as an *aide mémoire* to the president, a faculty committee drew up a memorial on the subject for the Board of Trustees and sent it on with the unanimous approval of the faculty. To give added momentum to the movement, the Medical faculty submitted a proposal to the Trustees that Dr. A. F. A. King undertake a solicitation of funds for a new medical building and addition to the Hospital. It was proposed that the Trustees borrow $200,000 at not more than 3½ or 4 per cent, to be repaid from the profits of the Hospital, with the interest guaranteed by fifty or more physicians on the staff. With this sum in hand, the mortgage on the stable site would be paid off, and a modern medical college building would be built, with private rooms and wards for clinical instruction. The matter was referred to the executive committee with power. The King proposal failed and a year later a much more ambitious proposal came from the Board itself: to borrow $360,000 instead of $200,000 at not more than 4 per cent.[14]

Although the faculty's proposal for the solicitation of funds by Dr. King for building came to naught, active discussion of plans for the proposed new buildings continued. These discussions were far enough advanced for the faculty to call in an architect, Mr. H. C. Hornblower, to give them his views. They turned later to another architect, Mr. Wood, to get the benefit of his ideas before going further because they had gone so far with Hornblower, but Wood refused to consider the matter. An opinion of Messrs. Cope and Stewardson of Philadelphia, however, approved a plan of open detached buildings instead of the solid front proposed by Hornblower. After considering all points of view, Dr. Carr of the faculty made a rough sketch that embodied the ideas of his colleagues, which Mr. Hornblower, the architect, was asked to elaborate with plans and elevations. The plans for the College and Hospital as thus drawn up were approved by the faculty and sent to the executive committee of the Board of Trustees.

Seven contractors submitted bids, specifying time for construction, cost of building the buildings separately, and cost for both. One fixed five months, another six, and five seven months as the time required. The cost for building the Hospital varied from $47,549 to $55,762; for the College, $77,385 to $94,031. Bids for building both varied from $122,934 to $141,667, heating not included in any bid. The actual cost was $156,-582.66.[15]

The faculty urged immediate construction so that the buildings would be ready by October, 1902. The dean, arranging for the storage of property at once, planned to finish the last few weeks of instruction, from March 31 to April 21, 1902, in other University buildings. The Dispensary was closed without any delay; the College building was closed March 22, and arrangements were made for closing the Hospital when feasible. If not otherwise provided for, nurses would be paid while the Hospital was closed. With a new Hospital about to be opened, it was decided to build up a nurses' school gradually, but until then to use the existing cooperative system. The salary of nurses was fixed at $7 per month after a probation period of two months.[16]

When Miss Odell, the superintendent of the Hospital, resigned early in 1903, it was decided thereafter to have a male superintendent of the Hospital and a superintendent of nurses and matron. Miss M. Paxton was appointed superintendent of nurses and matron for six months at $50 per month, Dr. Macatee as superintendent of the Hospital at $65 per month, and Miss Bowers as assistant matron at $30 per month.

Prices for rooms were fixed at from $15 to $75 per week for suites, "with instructions to the Superintendent to use a certain amount of discretion and maintain prices as high as possible." It was deemed inadvisable to admit patients of homeopathic physicians to the Hospital. A "Mr. Cooper" offered to furnish a horse and driver for an ambulance at $1 per trip, and the purchase of an ambulance, not to cost more than 400, was authorized.

On February 28, 1903, when the Hospital and new Medical College building were formally opened, thousands of visitors inspected the new structures. The first patient was received in the Hospital at 8 P.M. that evening.[17]

The last year of the Medical School's tenancy of the old building was apparently a prosperous one. A balance of $10,000 for the school year was reported, permitting a dividend of $900.[18]

In spite of the fact that the Medical School was running with apparent success and complete solvency in the traditional way, a defensive mood seemed to prevail in the years preceding the building of the new School. As changes were suggested there was the frequent caveat: provided that this is in accord with the rules of the Association of American Medical Colleges. The major cause for concern is perhaps revealed by a *Minute* of the meeting of December 9, 1899, listing the members of a committee appointed to prepare a reply to "Mr. Ingalls from the committee of the American Medical Association" with reference to night schools.

The Medical School was here confronting a problem which, at some time or other, practically every school in the University has had to face. It is not unfair to say that the problem as it arose with Columbian–George Washington was a very special one, due to the fact that "night students" so-called were largely employees of the federal government. In its earlier history, the hours scheduled for lectures had been frequently changed from forenoon to late afternoon to fit the convenience of the lecturers, who were for the most part practicing physicians in the District. Dissecting rooms were usually available throughout the day and into the evening, with demonstrators present at scheduled hours. As has been stated before, the Civil War brought about a change in the character of a large segment of the student body. Because of the tremendous increase in the size of the Civil Service, thousands of people were brought to

Washington who not only filled jobs, but whose appetite for personal enrichment, further education, and professional training was whetted by the relative security of government employment, the comparative adequacy of government pay in hard cash, the brevity of the government working day, the absence of entertainment in the city, and, as the University saw its opportunity, the availability of academic and professional courses. Frankly, one of the more cogent reasons for moving all of the units of the University to the center of the city was to cater to the convenience of their clientele. Government offices in those more leisurely days closed in mid-afternoon, making attendance at 4 or 4:30 P.M. classes quite possible

There was yet another factor. Not all of the government personnel was on the clerk level. Specialists, many of them of very great distinction, were being called to Washington as the Smithsonian and the scientific branches extended and developed their activities in research and publication. Here was a vast reservoir from which individuals of great talent and distinction could be drawn to enrich the offerings, direct research, and give advanced courses in virtually any field. These experts also had free time, thanks to the government's short working day. To have failed to utilize these individuals would have been folly. Special circumstances fostered in Washington the development of a true urban university not quite like any other in the country, and the term "night student" required special definition that was not always understood. It is true there were pros and cons, but the cons were not as overwhelming as many thought. Hence the problem of the "night schools": hence the defensive posture. In the development of medical education, the "night student" was to play a disappearing role.

The faculty *Minutes* around the turn of the century show a deep and constant concern for the improvement of teaching in the School. Actions taken were examined to see that they conformed to the rules of the Association of American Medical Colleges. Particularly active at this time was Professor W. W. Johnston in urging upon his colleagues the need for reappraisal of the work of their respective chairs. Each professor was instructed to draw up in writing a plan for the improvement of teaching in his field. These reports were brought in and discussed by the faculty at their meetings. By way of suggestion Professor Johnston prepared and presented an elaborate report on the methods used in teaching medicine in other institutions. He urged that "the teaching be objective and clinical as far as deemed practical and expedient." A special appropriation of $200 was made to each chair for added assistants, materials, or whatever was thought necessary to improve the work.

On February 16, 1901, the faculty had a long discussion of the possible effects of certain articles under discussion by the Association in regard to evening lectures and of the advisability of changing the hours. Two months later there was another lengthy discussion of other proposed amendments in the rules of the Association; and the dean, by way of documenting the faculty's views, was instructed "to prepare a list of the prominent alumni and so forth to be printed, if necessary." A committee was appointed to draw up the proper covering letter.

At this juncture, a letter was received from Dr. Ingalls of the Association of American Medical Colleges with reference to proposed amendments to the Association's constitution in which he expressed a willingness to be fair and grant certain concessions to the School. At the same meeting, the letter which had been prepared showing the good record of the School and why it did good work was read.

When the Association of American Medical Colleges met at St. Paul in June, 1901, the proposed amendments were voted down, leaving the constitution unchanged and admitting the southern Association. For the time being the *status quo* was maintained, but the faculty was not inclined to lower its guard. As an example, the dean was asked to publish a note in *Science* pointing out the standing of graduates before Army and Navy boards. The question of day vs. evening lectures still remained a constant subject for faculty discussion, though it was decided that no change in the lecture schedule would be made before the School was fully established in its new quarters. For the year 1903-1904 the faculty took a significant step. More day teaching was offered, with one course beginning at 9:30 A.M., the other at 4:30 P.M.[19] The faculty's action was formally approved by the Trustees in a resolution authorizing classroom work in medicine in the morning hours, in addition to that given in the late afternoon, for those giving their full time to study.[20]

CHAPTER THIRTEEN

More Stately Mansions

What had happened to the physical plant on the north side of H Street between 13th and 14th Streets defied simple description. In 1902, the Medical School building which had been given by Mr. Corcoran in 1865 and later expanded and remodeled was torn down. The lot on which this building stood was at the corner of a 15-foot alley with a frontage of 50 feet and a depth of 86 feet. Immediately to the rear of this lot was another with 58 feet on the alley running north and south and 50 feet on the alley running east and west. It was this second lot which the faculty had so often asked the University to acquire for purposes of expansion. Mr. Corcoran deeded it to the University in 1887. The new Medical School, which was to house the Department for seventy years, exactly covered the two lots given by Mr. Corcoran.

"The new building for the Department of Medicine," stated the catalogue, "is 50 by 144 feet, five stories in height, with four large lecture halls, accommodating from 200 to 350 students each, large laboratories for chemistry, pharmacy, histology, physiology, bacteriology, pathology, and anatomy; reception rooms, professors' rooms, museum and reading rooms, and study rooms."

In the same catalogue number, two pages later, we are told: "The faculty take pleasure in announcing that the new building of the Department of Dentistry is now completed and occupied. The building is 50 feet by 144 feet, five stories in height, of fireproof construction, and with every facility for the instruction and comfort of the students. There are four large lecture halls, with modern heating and ventilating appliances. The laboratories for Chemistry, Histology, Physiology, Bacteriology, Pathology, and Anatomy are models of their kind, while the operative and prosthetic technical laboratories are thoroughly equipped for Technic instruction.

"The Dental Infirmary is 50 feet by 75 feet on the third floor; in order to have an unobstructed light, it has large windows on three sides, there are adjoining prosthetic laboratories, separate laboratories for students and patients, and lockers sufficiently high to accommodate a dental engine. In fact, everything is provided to insure the comfort and convenience of all who occupy or visit this portion of the building."[1]

That the descriptions of the Medical Building and of the Dental Building were similar in so many details was more than coincidental, since both of the departments used the same building, or, as it worked out in practice, the Dental Department was the guest of the Medical Department in the new structure. That, indeed, was a major factor when, almost twenty years later, inadequate space and funds made it impossible to meet any longer, without radical change, the increasingly higher demands of professional education. The Dental School was discontinued, as will be discussed later, and the space thus released and the increased University support were diverted to the Medical School to permit it to maintain the standards of an effective teaching institution.[2]

On the lot immediately to the west of the Medical School and tied in with the old Prep building, which had been overhauled to serve as an ad interim hospital, was erected the new University Hospital which was opened concurrently with the new Medical School building. This lot, previously occupied by the Widdicombe stable, with a frontage of 100 feet on H Street and a depth of 145 feet running back to the alley on the north, was purchased by the University in 1897.[3]

The Hospital building was 60 by 80 feet, five stories in height. The catalogue, in a rather cheerful vein, described it as "fire-proof in construction, with the most modern private and public wards, with private baths and all modern improvements for ventilation, heating, etc. The public as well as private wards have delightful sun parlors, and every effort is employed to make the Hospital home-like."[4]

Doors were cut through from the old Prep building to the Hospital so that some of the space could be used for the activities of the Hospital. The major function of this building was to serve as the University Dispensary. Its central location in the city, conveniently served by public transportation, and its very ready acceptance by the public brought to it vast numbers of patients. Those who were connected with the University in those days have recalled how the officials of the financial institution next door at the corner of 14th Street frequently requested, on days when an especially large number of patients were waiting, that as many as possible would be taken indoors and the waiting queue turned down toward 13th Street. They feared that some alarmist would spread the rumor that a run on the bank was in progress.

Such then was the finished façade along H Street of the area where the activities of the Medical School were based for more than a century, from the end of the Civil War to the days of a war in southeastern Asia that had trouble finding an end.

The National Medical College made overtures in 1902 through the Board of Trustees for the union of this institution with the Columbian Medical School. While this college bore a name which was the same as a part of the cumbersome designation used for years by the Medical Department of Columbian, it was a school of much more recent origin. National's desire was that should it be discontinued, its students be accepted without loss of standing if admitted to Columbian. The faculty agreed to accept these students, provided there was no violation of Columbian's rules for advanced standing. The consolidation of the National Medical School and the Columbian Medical School was formally approved in September, 1903.[5]

Among the many changes in a period of change was a change in the name of the University: Columbian University became George Washington University. While this change could be explained in the light of the University's mission and tradition and by a desire to prevent confusion with an older university bearing a similar name, the real reason is more likely to be found in the financial difficulties of the institution at the time. It may seem strange to mention such difficulties along with a discussion of the construction of a new Medical building and Hospital. There were such difficulties and they were critical. Briefly the situation was this. When the original grounds and buildings on College Hill were sold, it was hoped that the proceeds of the sale would in large measure meet the cost of building a new home for the institution downtown. Exceedingly expensive real estate was acquired, and two buildings, one of them very large and impressive, were erected, taking in about a quarter of a large square at 15th and H Streets. The proceeds of the sale of the College Hill property came far from meeting the cost of relocation of the College downtown on the south side of H Street between 14th and 15th Streets. To this debt was added the cost of developing the Medical School's plant on the square below on the north side of H Street, between 13th and 14th Streets. These very considerable debts were consolidated in a "floating debt" which continued to grow in size with every renegotiation until the University was in a position where it could no longer pay even the interest.

The University had not been wise in its financial administration. It had been prone to meet operating deficits with funds restricted for other purposes. But the way had seemed clear. President Welling was a man with educational vision and wide contacts and by his side stood the generous president of the corporation, Mr. W. W. Corcoran. But this effective team could not go on forever and death brought it to a close. President Welling's successor, Dr. Whitman, was saddled with the ambitious but uncompleted plans of the imaginative Welling. Whitman had no Corcoran by his side; in fact, the University had to wait until well into the present century before another benefactor of the same order appeared. After a few discouraging years, Whitman resigned and was succeeded by the dean of the Law School, Dr. Charles W. Needham, who lacked nothing by way of energy but could not raise funds.

Welling himself toward the end of his long administration had seen the need of establishing some new and regular source of financial support. He turned to the Baptists and through their education society tried to kindle Baptist interest up to the contributory point in support of an institution whose founding they had fostered. Whitman, a clergyman of that denomination, tried so completely to get Baptist aid that for a few years the charter was amended, giving Baptists control of the Board of Trustees. There was much Baptist sympathy, but no dollars, and the charter was changed back to its original form.

While one source after another was being sought for financial assistance, a group of patriotic ladies, joined together in the George Washington Memorial Association, approached the University with what appeared a very attractive offer. Among other provisions in this offer, the Columbian University was to change its name to George Washington University in perpetuity and, on land made available by the University, the Association would build a $500,000 building in honor of Washington for the University's use. The University bought the lot for the building (the Pan American Union stands on the site) and changed its name in 1904. The monogram CU on the iron balusters of the steps in the Medical School reminded the students as long as they occupied the building that the University had once been called Columbian.

When Columbian College became Columbian University, President Welling had brought forward his "University Plan," which involved the creation of a series of graduate schools offering the most advanced instruction and conducting research in the arts and sciences, medicine, and law. Welling's "University Plan" was inherited by President Whitman, and passed on in turn by him to President Needham. The Medical faculty had been cautious in their approach to the plan when first presented to them, pleading lack of space and resources as their reasons for delaying affirmative action. The faculty included men of great distinction as scientists and investigators. To cite but one field, the successive professors of bacteriology and pathology from 1886 well into the present century were Theobald Smith (1859-1934), Walter Reed (1851-1902), James Carroll (1854-1907), and Frederick Fuller Russell (1870-1960). The presence of men of this caliber on the faculty stimulated a demand for study and research in medical science looking toward the degree of Doctor of Philosophy.[6]

The creation of the School of Graduate Studies in 1893 made such work possible on a limited basis. In 1898, the faculty informed the graduate dean that because of crowded conditions in the laboratories no general rules could be laid down, but that each case must be considered individually. The idea of a graduate school lingered for some time. On February 20, 1904, the Trustees passed an ordinance for the organization of such a school to be designated the "Department of Public Health," offering the higher degrees of Master of Public Health and Doctor of Public Health to candidates already holding a baccalaureate in Arts or Sciences and the degree of Doctor of Medicine. Section 15 of the ordinance, however, provided that it would not go into effect until an endowment of $200,000 had been pledged, or a guarantee fund subscribed to yield at least $5,000 a year for five years. An announcement of this ordinance was published in the annual catalogue of March, 1904, but the funds were not forthcoming. In increasing number, students were admitted to the School of Graduate Studies for advanced study and research in medical science leading to the degree of Doctor of Philosophy. Among the distinguished names in this category at a later date was that of Julius Axelrod, Ph.D., Nobel Laureate in Medicine (1970).[7]

On February 15, 1904, Dean deSchweinitz died at the early age of forty. Speaking at a memorial meeting, Dr. Charles Wardell Stiles remarked that Dr. deSchweinitz had frequently said that he disliked writing for publication, that his marked preference was to spend his time in the classroom and laboratory. In spite of his preference, deSchweinitz left a substantial contribution of sixty-four monographs. While he considered as most important his work on immunity, almost half of his papers dealt with tuberculosis. The *Minutes* of the Trustees referred to the fact that "the new buildings now occupied by the Medical School and the University Hospital were erected at his earnest solicitation. They were planned under his direction and erected under his personal supervision. These buildings must, in a measure, be considered memorials to his abiding interest in the Medical School and his foresight of the growth and needs of the department."[8]

CHAPTER FOURTEEN

Crisis

While the first decade of the twentieth century was one of many changes for the Medical School, it was one of continued crisis for the University, and from the effects of this the School was not immune. Three factors accounted in large measure for the University's plight. First, it had but a pitiful endowment and that was being constantly drawn upon to meet operating deficits. Second, the assembling of all the units of the University downtown and the large amount of necessary construction had involved both the expenditure of large sums, in excess of what had been realized by the sale of other property, and also increased costs for maintenance. Third, the hoped-for revitalization of the undergraduate College did not come about.

A word of explanation about this third factor is necessary. President Welling had been firm in his belief that the work of the University should be given in some central location, convenient to those who sought it and were willing to pay the cost. He saw hundreds of civil servants coming to the University for its instruction. He was quite right, but the undergraduate College was not benefited to anything like the degree expected. Quite likely, it needed the support of dormitory facilities which had been traditional but which did not exist on H Street. The other schools, particularly the Law School, did benefit. Work in the College was given at traditional hours and, for years, women were not admitted. The Corcoran Scientific School, organized in 1884, did admit women and offered all of its classes at the later hours. The College showed no growth and its operating deficit steadily mounted, to the increasing embarrassment of a University already heavily in debt.

President Needham came to a conviction at variance with a distinguished predecessor's ideas. President Welling thought that the University's future was in its graduate and professional work, not in its undergraduate College. Needham, frustrated at every turn in his efforts to get funds, felt that a major reason why the University had not drawn support from heavy donors was that it was known as "a night school." He undertook an active and successful campaign to change this. He was determined that no classroom work should be given at night in any part of the University, apparently considering 6:30 P.M. as the hour that separated day from night. To give the College a traditional appearance and manner, he went into an ambitious program for the encouragement of student activities. As Needham's days as president came toward an end, he could point with pride to the fact that, although there had been nothing in 1900, there were then in 1910 sixteen fraternities, three sororities, four debating societies, football, baseball, track, rifle, some boating, and a weekly and annual publication.[1] In his fervor, President Needham must have evangelized even the Medical faculty, for on one occasion the faculty appropriated $60 for the Athletic Association to be paid by them to Columbian College on the account of the fees of a very well-known athlete.[2]

Reference was made in an earlier chapter to the fear of the Medical faculty in 1899 to 1901 that action would be taken by the Association of American Medical Colleges at its 1901 meeting in St. Paul to put into effect constitutional changes contrary to the interests of the Medical School. The changes were voted down, so the immediate threat with reference to evening lectures ended for the time. The pressure, however, continued from the professional association, now augmented by Needham's intention to eliminate anything that might suggest "a night school." A report of the president to the Trustees on November 16, 1904, stated that the Dental School, which then had 63 students, had been taken off the list of their National Association because of evening work.[3]

Records of the Trustees show the wavering policy that the Medical School had to pursue. Needham had, no doubt, thought that the end he sought was well in sight when in 1906 he told his Board of Trustees that George Washington was no longer a night school or a University whose prime purpose was to educate government clerks. Questions of standards and schedules, however, had a financial aspect. As desirous as Needham was of garbing himself in what he assumed were the authentic habiliments of academic acceptability, he could not forget that students paid tuition and students must not be driven away when so much depended upon income from student fees.

Acting on recommendations, the Trustees on January 8, 1908, announced the policy that beginning with the session of 1909-1910, all medical work would be on a full-time basis, with two years of college or the equivalent required for admission. On May 7 of the same year, they adopted the policy that beginning with the session of 1908-1909, the Medical School would be a full-time school. In April of 1909, it was announced that advanced requirements for law and medicine had been postponed until a later time to be decided upon by the faculties.[4]

Belatedly steps were taken to inform the senior members of the faculties of the crucial state of the University's finances. In November, 1908, and again in April, 1909, the Board, asking that no information be given to the press, directed the administration to consult with the senior professors. Zero hour was approaching. The limit of borrowing had been reached. Unless the miraculous happened there would be no funds to pay the faculties after April, 1910.

Needham worked feverishly to get funds: from individual givers, the Baptist denomination, the George Washington Memorial Association, the Congress by way of land-grant funds under the Morrill Act, and by radical cuts in the budget. It is hard to imagine anyone more completely unsuccessful. Of all these moves, budget-cutting was the straw that broke the camel's back. An administrative committee went over the faculty lists with a red pencil. Its radical recommendations, embodying Needham's ideas, were adopted. One of these recommendations required detailed attention.

Two senior professors, men of marked eminence, Dr. James Howard Gore and Dr. James McBride Sterrett, were retired on Carnegie pensions. These men were productive scholars with wide personal contacts, and in the full vigor of their intellectual power. The reason for their involuntary retirement was not that they had been critical of the administration (they had). By eliminating two top faculty salaries a considerable saving would be effected because their work could be carried by a recent appointee and a part-time instructor.[5]

This attempt at economy was to have grave consequences. The first major retirement plan for college teachers in the United States was launched in 1905 at the instance of Mr. Andrew Carnegie, who gave the funds for financing it. It was believed that there were only 92 private and nonsectarian institutions of higher learning that were qualified by their academic standing to meet the requirements of the Carnegie Foundation for admission to its pension system. In general, this system provided for the payment of a pension on a noncontributory basis to professors retired at the age of 65 after at least thirty years of service, the pension to be equal to no more than half the average annual salary during the five years prior to retirement.[6]

After doubts raised by the Foundation had been quieted by a formal resolution of the Trustees that the University was free of all sectarian control and tests, George Washington was admitted to the Carnegie pension system, but not for long.

The Needham administration had been under constant fire and the forced retirement of two honored teachers led to protests from every side. Dr. Henry S. Pritchett, head of the Carnegie Foundation, had a survey of the University made, and on the basis of its findings wrote a letter to President Needham dated June 4, 1909. No communication could have been more devastating. He informed President Needham "that the relation of the George Washington University as an accepted institution is terminated with this date."

Dr. Pritchett's criticisms were all-encompassing. With reference to the retirement of the two professors, the University had struck "a blow at academic dignity and academic freedom." The productive endowment had fallen well below the minimum requirement of the Foundation. Except in the undergraduate College which admitted "with reasonable regard" to requirements, announced standards of admission were not enforced. In the case of each of the schools he particularized. Two sentences expressed his judgment on the Medical School. "Similarly in the Medical School, the announced requirements for admission have been repeatedly evaded. If the entrance requirements to this School were actually enforced, the enrollment would be so greatly reduced that the department could not continue: a result, I may add, entirely in the interest of medical education since the District of Columbia and the region about it are oversupplied not only with physicians but with weak medical schools."

In the following year (1910) appeared the famous Bulletin Number Four: *Medical Education in the United States and Canada; a Report to the Carnegie Foundation for the Advancement of Teaching,* by Abraham Flexner, with an Introduction by Henry S. Pritchett, president of the Foundation. Part II of this highly influential report surveyed the medical schools of the United States and Canada by states and provinces, with "general considerations" for each political unit. The visit to George Washington University to gather data for the report was made in March, 1909. This report, when read along with those on other institutions, did not seem too unfavorable in its references to laboratory and clinical facilities. On the question of finances, it gave figures, but no comment. For entrance requirements no comment was needed: "Less than a four-year high school course." For teaching staff, the point of criticism was obvious: "69 instructors, 25 being professors, none of whom is a full-time teacher; three instructors of other grade devote entire time to school." Under "general considerations," Flexner found that Howard Medical School "has a distinct mission—that of training the Negro physician—and an assured future."

"The other two schools [i.e., George Washington and Georgetown] lack adequate resources as well as assured prospects. They are surrounded by medical schools—those of Richmond, Baltimore, Philadelphia—whose competition they cannot meet. Finally, the District of Columbia has relatively more physicians than any other part of the country. Should the District require, as it ought, a higher basis, or even enforce an actual four-year high school standard, both would suffer seriously. Neither school is now equal to the task of training physicians of modern type."

Such dismal observations were by no means restricted to the two schools in the District of Columbia, nor by any means were they the sharpest of the criticisms made on medical schools throughout the States and the Dominion. On the basis of socioeconomic and professional and academic criteria that he had established, Dr. Flexner was convinced of the need for a radical reduction in the number of medical schools. "Reduction of our 155 medical schools to 31," he wrote, "would deprive of a medical school no section that is now capable of maintaining one."

It is quite clear that the observations made by Pritchett in his letters to Needham were based on Flexner's report on his visit to the University three months before.[7]

With a great show of independence President Needham declared that no one could dictate to the University about its retirement policy or its finances. One possibility for financial aid had not been finally blocked: he worked on the members of the Congress for passage of the Gallinger-Boutell Amendment to the Morrill Act which would designate George Washington as the institution in the District to receive the annual appropriations provided by the act. Massive opposition soon blocked him here, but apparently nothing blocked Needham's detractors and the University's critics.

At its meeting on April 27, 1910, the Board of Trustees heard two letters. The first was the resignation of Charles Willis Needham from the presidency; the second was the announcement from the Attorney General of the United States that, pursuant to a resolution adopted by the House of Representatives April 25, 1910, he was about to proceed to an investigation of the financial condition of the University. This action was taken in accordance with the wide powers given to the Attorney General by Section 10 of the charter of 1821.

The detailed investigation by the Attorney General as reported to the House of Representatives showed that the University had used its endowment and other restricted funds to make up deficits in operating expenses. On the institution was placed the responsibility of restoring the funds that had been improperly applied. There followed cutbacks in faculty, organizational consolidations, and the sale of University property. The Law School and the University Building on H Street between 14th and 15th Streets were sold and the proceeds applied to the debt and to the restoration of endowments as far as they would go. A mortgage was placed on the medical property between 13th and 14th Streets to cover the additional amount of indebtedness. This mortgage was paid off during the Marvin administration.

A major operation had been performed on the University. It really had no funds, but it was no longer pressed by debts. Only the Medical School retained its old quarters; the other schools were in temporary, rented locations. Although all of its shortcomings had been aired, the Medical School still had a home.[8]

It might be well at this point to turn away from this narrative of University crises and look specifically at the Medical School. The successor of Dr. deSchweinitz as dean was William Fowke Ravenel Phillips (1863-1934), a Virginian by birth and a graduate of the Medical School in the class of 1890. He had been prosector of anatomy, 1890-1891, then professor of hygiene, 1891-1892, and of practical anatomy, 1905-1909. In the interval 1895-1904 he was medical climatologist in the United States Weather Bureau. Dr. Phillips served as dean, 1904-1909. In later years he taught at the University of Alabama, the Medical College of South Carolina, and Georgetown University.

During Dean Phillips' tenure two new educational units were added to the University as affiliated colleges. Section 2 of an act of Congress,

Pennsylvania Avenue from Washington Circle at 23rd Street Looking Down
Toward 17th Street *c.* 1920.

Cloyd Heck Marvin, President of the University, 1927-1959.

Oswald Symister Colclough, Acting President, 1959-1961, 1964-1965.

Thomas Henry Carroll, President of the University, 1961-1964.

Lloyd Hartman Elliott, President of the University, 1965-

Earl Baldwin McKinley, M.D., Dean of the School of Medicine, 1931-1938.

Walter Andrew Bloedorn, M.D., Dean of the School of Medicine, 1938-1957.

John L. Parks, M.D., Dean of the School of Medicine, 1957-1972; Vice President for Medical Affairs, 1972.

James Joseph Feffer, M.D., Acting Dean of the School of Medicine, 1972; Vice President for Medical Affairs, 1972-

Foreground, The Paul Himmelfarb Health Sciences Library, 1973; *backgrou*

he Walter G. Ross Hall, 1973. These are on 23rd, 24th, H, and Eye Streets.

University Hospital, at Washington Circle, 22nd, 23rd, Eye Streets and Pennsylvania Avenue, 1948.

Meyer Pavilion, the University Hospital, 22nd Street Between Eye Street and Pennsylvania Avenue, 1965.

Warwick Memorial, Washington Circle, 1954.

Entrance to the H. B. Burns Memorial Building, the University Clinic, Corner of 22nd Street and Pennsylvania Avenue.

The Watson W. Wise Emergency Pavilion, University Hospital, Washington Circle, 1971.

approved March 3, 1905, and supplementing the original charter of
1821, provided that, with the University's consent, colleges carrying on
special lines of educational work could be made "educationally a part
of the system of the University, but upon independent financial foundations."[9]

Under provision of this act, the National College of Pharmacy became an affiliated college. The original College owed its origin to the
Columbian Pharmaceutical Association and received its first students in
November, 1872. On November 22, 1905, the Board of Trustees incorporated the National College of Pharmacy, which retained the same
name, into the University. The College building was on the south side
of Eye Street, between 8th and 9th Streets.[10]

Under the same provision, the College of Veterinary Medicine's
charter was adopted on March 17, 1908, and this College was incorporated into the University as an affiliated institution, related educationally
but fully autonomous financially. Negotiations with the College of
Veterinary Medicine had been in process for years. Because of the important research being carried on by the Bureau of Animal Industry of
the Department of Agriculture, there were many personal ties and
considerable cooperation between the veterinary specialists in the Bureau
and the Medical faculty. During his entire tenure in the School, Dean
deSchweinitz, for example, was at the same time an important scientific investigator of the Bureau of Animal Industry. The way to union had first
been opened in 1896 when the Trustees voted to accept the faculty and
the curriculum of the National Veterinary College. Its relationship to
the University was to be the same as that of the Law, Dental, and
Medical Schools, that is, no financial risk to the University was involved.
The Veterinary College, however, was unwilling to give up its identity
and become a department of the University. The charter amendment
took care of the situation. The College retained its identity and its
financial autonomy *within* the University structure as an affiliated
college.[11]

In addition to the two affiliated colleges, a new unit in the Medical
Department was organized in 1903. A School for Nurses was established, with Miss Minnie Paxton serving as superintendent of nurses. She
was succeeded July 1, 1904, by Miss Mary Belle Struble. From the
beginning the Nurses Home at 1328 Eye Street had been found inadequate because of limited study space for the pupil nurses. It was not
until 1913, through the purchase of 1016 13th Street and 1300 L Street,

that adequate quarters were obtained. At the end of the second year the personnel of the School consisted of a superintendent of nurses, a head nurse, 22 pupils, and 5 probationers.[12]

To be admitted, an applicant must be between the ages of 21 and 35 and have sufficient preliminary education to profit by the course. During a probationary period of two months, probationers would receive board, lodging, laundry, and free medical attention. If accepted as fitted for the duties of nursing, a probationer then became a pupil nurse, receiving $5 a month during the first year, $7 during the second year, and $9 the third year to cover expenses of uniforms and textbooks. Pupil nurses were on duty for twelve hours, 7:30 to 7:30, with one to two hours off for rest and recreation, with one-half day off each week and four hours off on Sunday. Two weeks' vacation a year, with three or four weeks for seniors, were allowed if hospital duties permitted. Instruction was supervised by the Medical faculty; it extended over a period of three years.[13]

It was hoped that the opening of this vastly enlarged Hospital of 100 beds would not complicate but perhaps rather ease the financial situation. Unfortunately its first year showed a small, but disheartening, deficit. It did add greatly to the facilities for clinical instruction, along with the arrangements made with Garfield, Children's, Central Dispensary and Emergency, Providence, Episcopal, Columbia and St. Elizabeth's Hospital, and the Lutheran Eye and Ear Infirmary. Two courses of lectures were given, beginning at 9:30 A.M. and 4:30 P.M. While there was a standing desire expressed in faculty resolutions to raise admissions requirements to include a two-year premedical course, financial considerations demanded delay. When in 1908 a full-time requirement was put into effect, there was a temporary reduction in the number of students. In the following year, evidence of proficiency in theoretical and organic chemistry, in addition to a high school diploma, was required for admission.[14]

The Dental School, on a more modest plane, was likewise raising its standards of admission. In 1904 it required a certificate of admission into the third year of standard high school work, or its equivalent.[15]

Dr. Phillips' brief tenure as dean ended while the University was involved in financial crisis. His years had not been particularly fruitful.

CHAPTER FIFTEEN

The New Relationship

On May 6, 1909, the Trustees elected William Cline Borden (1858-1934) dean of the Medical School, an office he was to hold until 1930. A graduate of the School in the class of '83, he passed the examinations and was appointed Acting Assistant Surgeon U.S.A. His first military service was in the frontier posts of the old West. The final destination of his journey to his first assignment was reached by stagecoach. In those early days, while serving in distant and widely separated posts, the young surgeon busily carried on his work in microscopy, contriving almost miraculously to keep his equipment with him wherever he happened to be stationed. Following the Spanish-American War, Major Borden was placed in command of the Army General Hospital at Washington Barracks and appointed professor of military surgery in the Army Medical School. In 1908 he was sent to the Philippines. While appearing before the promotion board to be advanced to the rank of Lieutenant Colonel, a heart condition, which had possibly been aggravated by tropical service, was noted and he was retired at the higher rank.

Dr. J. Ford Thompson, who had served with great distinction as professor of surgery since 1872, had but recently died and his successor was to be named by the Trustees at their spring meeting in 1909. Dr. Borden was proposed as Dr. Thompson's successor. There was really not one vacancy, but two.

It became known that Dean Phillips would not be reappointed because of sharp differences of opinion with President Needham. Registration in the Medical School had been plummeting downward. From the 1905 catalogue on, each year had shown a significant decline: 298, 280, 225,

198, 156, 115, indicating public alarm and loss of confidence. The School ran over its budgetary allotments and the Hospital incurred regular deficits. The question of "night students" still remained to be solved in a way that would convince the accrediting agency. With this drab situation all too obvious, Dr. Borden was asked if he would accept both the position of the chair of surgery and the deanship.

It was a happy day for the Medical School when Dr. Borden accepted the two posts, becoming dean on June 15, 1909. As he reported to the president, he "found the School inefficiently organized and generally in bad shape." Informed for the first time, since the original letter had never been brought to his attention, that the Council on Medical Education had received no word as to the correction of deficiencies they had pointed out and that failing to receive this they could not place the School on the accepted list as "Class A," Dean Borden appeared before the Council, explained the circumstances, pointed out the improvements that had been made, and secured the Class A rating. His first major faculty appointment was that of the distinguished scientist, Dr. Frederick F. Russell, professor of bacteriology and pathology in the Army Medical School and curator of the Army Medical Museum.

Speaking before the George Washington University Medical Society on April 26, 1910, Dean Borden delivered what was, in terms of timing and breadth of range, his inaugural address. In that address he laid down, as his conclusions, what were to be basic requirements:

1. It is no longer possible to conduct an adequate Medical School on a commercial basis.
2. A Medical School should now be considered a school of applied science.
3. A Medical School should be an integral part of a university.
4. A minimum entrance requirement of four years' high school should be strictly enforced.

While the dean did not particularize, the background for his observations was the deficiencies of ninety years of Medical School history. That he met his own objectives marks him as one of the truly great administrators in the University's history.[1]

In the sad financial state of the University at the time, austerity was the rule all around and reform had to proceed slowly. Accordingly an ordinance adopted by the Board of Trustees in 1910 provided that the finances of the Medical and Dental Schools should be handled in a single account. For the coming academic year, members of the faculty were to be paid one-half of their allowed salaries. The balance remaining at the end of the year was to be applied to: (1) repayment of $2,000 advanced to the Medical School by the University, (2) payment of salaries in full, (3) a fund for future needs. The following year, the Law and Medical faculties asked that all student fees be devoted to the School which collected them, with the exception of its share of the general administrative overhead of the University. After some months' delay, the Trustees agreed.[2]

Important victories in the struggle to maintain permanently a fully accredited Medical School had been gained, but the war had not yet been won. The approach and spread of a world-wide conflict imposed for the time a moratorium as far as the Medical School went. Faced with imminent danger to the national security, President Stockton had defined the University's stance on the day following President Wilson's war message to Congress:

We approve and endorse the message yesterday submitted to the Congress by the President of the United States, and pledge to him as Commander-in-Chief of the Army and Navy our loyal support in the due execution of his office and in his endeavor to guard the interests and integrity of our country.[3]

Dean Borden was called to active duty as a Lieutenant Colonel and assigned to Walter Reed General Hospital in charge of surgical service. The superintendent of the hospital, Captain John Bruce Copping, was also called to active duty. To prevent the college classrooms of the country from being emptied of all male students through the operation of the draft, the government set up the Students' Army Training Corps and a similar Naval Unit. By this arrangement regularly admitted college students could enlist for military service but remained in their classes until defense requirements made their active duty necessary. These students received food and quarters at the College, and military allowances. By dint of herculean effort on the part of the University administration, facilities for feeding and housing these student soldiers were provided; the Army and Navy units were activated in the beginning of the 1918-1919 session. The catalogue shows 75 medical and 65 dental students in the SATC and 3 medical and 7 dental students in the Naval Unit. The collapse of the Central Powers fortunately brought the return of peace after one semester of service on the part of the student soldiers.

Even so short an experience proved disruptive to the orderly progress of academic work. There was, however, another equally disruptive force and the two, operating concurrently, produced a period of crisis for the University and for its Hospital. The peak of the great Spanish influenza epidemic coincided with the later months of the World War. On October 9, 1918, it was reported to the Board of Trustees that the suspension of all academic work had been required by the Health Department on account of the epidemic. Because of this four-week suspension, the academic year was not ended until June 18, 1919.[4]

The Hospital was struck particularly hard by the epidemic. The daily press reported that the members of the staff, sadly depleted by the war conditions and by illness, were working around the clock and, weakened by their labors, were becoming easy victims of the disease. Twenty-four nurses were prostrated by the influenza; and Miss Mary Glasscock, the superintendent of nurses, and Dr. Thomas Miller, Jr., of the staff died.

In a letter written to Dr. D. L. Borden from the Hospital on September 23, 1918, Miss Glasscock gave a moving picture of the situation in the Hospital and the Medical School. She went over the staff and mentioned one after another of the men leaving for military service, wondering who would take their places. "Each day the ranks thin out just a little more and all the time we are made to realize the vastness of the situation more and more." Again she writes, "No janitors or orderlies and every one says it will be worse." There is a somberness about her letter, yet she was not defeated; only death did that.[5]

In the decade preceding the entry of the United States into the World War, the number of dental students had shown a steady increase—from 28 in 1910 to 152 in the peak year of 1918. As gratifying as that increase was in many ways, it did intensify a problem which was vital. In each one of his annual reports from the first on, Dean Borden had made emphatic statements about the Medical School's need for more room. The financial situation had forced the Medical School to continue to house the Chemistry Department of Arts and Sciences in its building. At the same time, the Dental School, established under the aegis of the Medical faculty, had from the beginning been housed in the same building. It had gradually built up a student body which, at times, exceeded in number that of the Medical School. Crowded conditions in the Medical building were becoming more intolerable year after year.

The graduating class of 1912 was the last to include among its members students who had taken the late courses. In the pre-World War I decade registration had been generally upward, except that with every change in admissions requirements there was a recession.

When in the beginning of Dean Borden's administration there was a tightening of the minimum requirement, when after January 1, 1914, the one-year college requirement including basic sciences was made effective, and when after January 1, 1918, the two-year pre-medical requirement was applied, there was in each case a drop in registration.

In 1904, the Dental School had been removed from the National Association's list because of its evening work. Some readjustments had been made and the School was restored to the list. As of July 24, 1916, it was rated Class A. On April 30, 1918, the dean reported to the Trustees that the Dental School had been transferred from the Class A to the Class C list. Dean Borden pointed out that if this status were continued, the Surgeon General would withdraw the very considerable number of enlisted men who were registered, thus reducing the School's income materially. He feared that if all late courses had to be abandoned, it would eliminate much of the School's normal clientele.[6]

On October 9, 1918, Carl Joseph Mess, D.D.S. 1902, was elected dean of the Dental School, succeeding Dr. Roland Walton. The University bulletin issued in March, 1918, instead of giving the detailed announcement for the coming year, had stated:

At the time of the present publication, as the Dental School is being completely reorganized on the basis of the requirements of the Dental Educational Council of America, it is not possible to publish the Bulletin of this School. At the beginning of the next term and year, the instruction of the Dental School will be carried on between 9 A.M. and 5:30 P.M. No night classes will be held or instruction given at night.[7]

It was, however, not the Dental School alone that was in jeopardy. As soon as he had returned to the Medical School after his wartime military service, Dean Borden had warned the University administration in no uncertain terms: "I feel that our classification cannot be much longer maintained." Within months an official inspection was made by Dr. William Pepper and Dr. N. P. Colwell for the American Medical Association. The inspectors' findings were discouraging: laboratory facilities "very meager," dispensary and hospital material "seriously deficient," essential minimum of full-time professors "lacking," library and museum "not satisfactory." Unless various changes were made—increase in finances, adequate number of full-time teachers, special provisions for dental students, a teaching hospital of adequate size—the School could not remain on the list of acceptable medical colleges. "The future prospects of this School are very unpromising." Such was their conclusion.

Dean Borden did not bandy words with the administration. He reiterated recommendations that had, in the main, been made almost a year earlier. But this time there was a new urgency—he had the leverage of the inspectors' findings. Their irreducible requirements were his recommendations, but in setting a time limit his recommendations became ultimata. The dean requested authority, unless the Trustees were prepared to take immediate action, "to inform the student body that the School will be reorganized before next session or will be discontinued after Commencement in June while still in Class 'A.' " He suggested that a forthright statement of the case be made to the press.

Parenthetically and for purposes of comparison, it is worthy to note that in this period of crisis tuition fees were increased: in the Medical School from $175 to $200, and in the Dental School from $150 to $175.[8]

In a five-hour session with the Trustees, Dean Borden, Dr. Oscar B. Hunter, and Dr. Sterling Ruffin hammered out the details which would permit the continuance of the School on a Class A basis. Because the timing was important to forestall any adverse action, the dean on March 21, 1920, wrote to Dr. N. P. Colwell, secretary of the Council on Education of the American Medical Association, stating that "it appears that the University is now willing to obligate itself to the following and soon announce it as a definite obligation of the Board of Trustees" and he listed ten provisions. Briefly they were:

1. A definite allotment of $25,000 annually over and above student fees and exclusive of the Hospital, making possible the employment of twelve full-time teachers and the formation of a properly staffed clinical division;

2. Discontinuance of the Dental School;

3. The turning over of the entire building to the Medical School, with necessary reconstruction of the interior at a cost of $4,000, the Arts and Sciences Chemistry Department to have use of the chemistry laboratory after 5 P.M., but with no joint teaching or mixing of students;

4. Development of a museum in proper quarters under the direction of the professor of pathology;

5. Rehabilitation and up-dating of the library, with a full-time librarian;

6. Adequate equipment of laboratory for physiological and clinical chemistry;

7. Increased care in admissions and advanced standing;

8. Adoption of policy for sale of present Medical School and Hospital property and erection of a new medical building and hospital;

9. Utilization of present clinics in existing hospitals to the greatest extent;

10. Continued attempts to form definite affiliation with good existing hospitals.

Dean Borden's letter ended with a direct question: "If action as above given is taken by the University authorities, can the School be continued in Class A?"

The dean's proposals were formally approved by the Board of Trustees on April 3, 1920. Lest it be felt that the Dental School was being dealt with too cavalierly, a committee of three was appointed to consult with the Dental faculty and report before May 15. Needless to say, the committee found no answer to a hopeless question.[9]

The Dental School was discontinued in 1921. During the thirty-four years of its existence it had conferred 313 degrees. Of its graduates, eleven had served as presidents of the District of Columbia Dental Society; and two of these, C. Willard Camalier, D.D.S. 1912, and Sterling V. Mead, D.D.S. 1914, had also been presidents of the American Dental Association.

The Trustees' resolution of April 3, 1920, confirming the assurances that Dean Borden had given in his letter to the Council on Education and pledging the good faith of the University in carrying them out, marks the Great Divide in the history of the Medical School. Understood in the beginning to obligate the University for five years, it was obvious that the arrangement having been made, its basic philosophy would not be changed. As significant as this action was, it must not be overrated. It did not solve the Medical School's problems, once and for all. It did not provide the large sums necessary for granting annual subsidies, for paying the salaries of a vastly expanded faculty, for providing for large-scale construction, or for acquiring expensive equipment. It did one essential thing. It insured the continued existence of the School as an accepted school with an opportunity to work its way to high distinction. In that continuing effort, it furnished the blueprint for development. What has happened in the last fifty years is the working out of that blueprint in tangible form and with increasingly adequate expression. The result has been the Medical Center.

There had been almost a century of Medical School history—before 1920. In the 1820's, a small group of medical men, operating under the charter rights of Columbian College in the District of Columbia, had organized a Medical Department. They provided, at their own expense, quarters for instruction and funds for the operation of the School, collected fees, and, when there was a surplus, distributed it among themselves. The College's relation to its Medical Department was slight and formal, limited to the conferring of degrees and to confirmation of faculty nominations. The fully proprietary character of the Medical School was diluted slowly, as preceding chapters have shown. The active factor was usually an economic one. When, thanks to the gift of Mr. Corcoran, the Medical Department was for the first time housed in a building belonging to the University, it became easier to bring the School more closely under control. To simplify the tax status of the medical property, the Medical School was formally declared an integral part of the University and its faculty were given the prima-facie status of members of the University teaching staff. Evidences of the old proprietary relationship still remained, as we have seen. The 1920 resolution made it obvious that the old regime was ended. The Medical School would not be self-supporting, let alone profit-making. Instead, it was guaranteed University funds over and above student fees for its development as a modern Medical School.

Many deserved credit for the successful outcome of the Medical School crisis, but none in larger measure than Dean Borden. A man of tremendous will power and determination, he had pressured both the Council on Education and the Board of Trustees to bring about the understanding that he desired. Many thought him rigid, inflexible, and unduly laconic in speech. Those who really knew him found him humane, sympathetic, and above all passionately loyal to the School. Students who as freshmen had quaked in his presence smiled with real affection and friendship when four years later he called upon them at Commencement to come forward to receive their "die-plomas."

Dr. Borden spent the first half of his term as dean (1909-1930) in tidying up administration and instruction in an organization which he had described "as inefficiently organized and generally in bad shape."

He had done this in the face of constantly increasing pressure to meet new professional standards without any increase in the resources at his command. He did the job so thoroughly that, when he came to the point of crisis, his ability and integrity had been so well demonstrated that he was able to convince his medical colleagues that a basis for permanent improvement had been laid and to persuade the University with its meager resources to provide means for building on that foundation. That was the task of the final decade of his tenure: to implement the assurances that he had given.

The basic problem was complex and bound to be costly in solution. The University Hospital was small and limited in its clinical facilities. Ideally the construction of a larger and more adequate hospital was indicated, or some viable substitute that could be worked out. At the same time a wider and more systematic utilization of clinics in existing hospitals and affiliations with good hospitals had to be considered.

Most serious attention was given to a Garfield–George Washington affiliation. This proposal seemed particularly attractive because of the Warwick bequest of more than a half-million dollars for a cancer hospital and laboratories in connection with the Washington Home for Foundlings. This fund, it was believed, could, by arrangement with the Home for Foundlings, be used by George Washington and Garfield to carry out the donor's intention. Brought to the Board of Trustees in the fall of 1926, this proposal was referred to a committee, which on January 19, 1927, submitted a report on the amalgamation of the George Washington and Garfield Memorial Hospitals and the Washington Home for Foundlings as a nucleus for a hospital center.

Basic articles for agreement were adopted. Each of the three institutions would continue its corporate existence and control, except that the University would control teaching rights, with the rights of the other Medical Schools insured by the inclusion of their representatives on the staff of the hospital. The University was to sell the medical property on H Street as soon as practicable, and erect a new Medical School in the vicinity of Garfield. Garfield was to lease at a reasonable rental land within its holding to the Washington Home for Foundlings for the erection of a hospital building for the care and treatment of women with cancer, to be known as the "Helen L. and Mary E. Warwick Memorial" and so indicated by lettering on the exterior of the building. The University would turn over to the new Hospital the income from its hospital endowment funds. The Nurses School was to be continued

as "the Washington Medical Center Nurses Training School." In anticipation of the building of a new Medical School, the University bought
lots on Sherman Avenue, north of Garfield Hospital and within the
same square, for $31,285, subject to a trust of $15,048. The property
was sold ten years later for $20,500.[10]

At the end of fiscal year 1926-1927, the brief administration of President William Mather Lewis (1923-1927) came to a close and the long
administration of President Cloyd Heck Marvin (1927-1959) began.
The new president did not share the enthusiasm for the Garfield plan.
By mutual consent the agreement was abrogated, negotiations were
terminated, and the parties found other solutions for their problems.[11]

The attempt to bring George Washington, Garfield, and the Warwick
Memorial together in a close working arrangement had really been an
effort to carry out one of the undertakings entered into by the University
in its announcement of policy in the agreement of 1920. To meet more
adequately its requirements for clinical instruction, among other efforts
that were made was to seek affiliation with a good existing hospital or
undertake the construction of a modern and adequate University Hospital.

The first alternative had been tried, embodying as it did the most favorable setup available in the area. It had involved long and intricate negotiations with the three institutions concerned, and an agreement was
arrived at, only to be canceled by mutual consent. The second alternative
remained, but seemed far off.

Academic progress had been made. The increasing numbers of applicants for medical education had made possible the raising of requirements to a satisfactory level and the highly selective acceptance of
candidates. In spite of what could be done administratively, there still
remained the antiquated, worn out, and inadequate plant. The road to
high distinction was still untrod.

CHAPTER SIXTEEN

End of the Midtown Era

The steps which forecast the approaching end of the midtown era and the final regrouping of all of the University's units on a single campus come within the long administration of the twelfth president of the University.

Cloyd Heck Marvin, although he had already held one university presidency, was yet a young man of thirty-eight when he became president of George Washington University. His administration of thirty-two years (1927-1959) was the longest in the history of the institution. During at least the first two decades of his tenure, he displayed a vigor, an imagination, a tenacity, and a determination almost without parallel. Marvin rejected the more limited and modest concepts of Dean Howard L. Hodgkins and his contemporaries which had been formed in days of great financial crisis and had saved the University in those trying times. He thought in terms of the larger and expanded University which has been realized since his time. But Marvin himself was not a free agent. He was in those early years a stalwart follower of Herbert Hoover and he resisted any inroads into the public purse, even when that purse began to be opened wide and others dipped into it without compunction.

He had to work with only the modest sums which his predecessors had been able by their parsimony to accumulate through low overhead, meager faculty salaries, and careful administration. His coming to office practically coincided with the beginning of the Great Depression. His early administration had to face the ups and downs as the economy struggled to its feet, only to be upset again by the prospect of foreign war and then by war itself. But he struggled through with it to find the economic hazards of a war period more than offset by vastly increased enrollments and government projects and grants which the public interest (and the University's) forced him, not too unwillingly, to accept. It was his proud boast, demonstrated by fact, that at no time in his administration were salaries cut and that he was able to keep intact for purposes of development the extraordinary income that came to the University.

The old order changed. The old deans passed away. When Mr. John Bell Larner, who had been chairman of the Board of Trustees for a generation, died and was succeeded by Mr. Robert V. Fleming, president of the Riggs National Bank, Marvin had at his side the vigorous support of Washington's most prominent banker, backed by his personal prestige and the power of the great financial institution that he headed.

For a year after Dean Borden's retirement the Medical School was administered by a triumvirate: Dr. Walter A. Bloedorn, Dr. Joseph H. Roe, and Dr. Oscar B. Hunter. On October 8, 1931, Dr. Earl Baldwin McKinley was appointed professor of bacteriology and dean of the Medical School. In some ways, Dean McKinley's coming inaugurated a renewal of interest in scientific investigation and research.

Dean McKinley was a graduate of the University of Michigan (A.B. 1916, M.D. 1922). He had been a Fellow of the National Research Council at the Pasteur Institute, University of Brussels, had taught at the Medical Schools of Michigan and Baylor, and at the College of Physicians and Surgeons at Columbia. At the time of his election as dean he was the director of the School of Tropical Medicine at the University of Puerto Rico under Columbia's auspices. His work in the Philippines as field director for the Rockefeller Foundation and at the School of Tropical Medicine in Puerto Rico had marked him out as an outstanding investigator particularly on leprosy and its related problems, especially the control of the disease. He was engaged in the pursuit of his scientific interest when he came to an untimely end in the summer of 1938.

Under his leadership there was a quickened interest in research. A four-story building was erected immediately to the rear of the Medical School at a cost of $60,000 to afford additional and badly needed laboratories. The increasingly important research activity of the faculty brought wide and favorable attention to the institution. Much of the important work of Dr. Vincent deVigneaud, Nobel Laureate in Chemistry in 1955, was done during the years 1932 to 1938 while he was professor of biochemistry in the Medical School.[1]

The School of Nursing was discontinued in 1931, and the Nurses Home property at 13th and L Streets was sold. The Medical ROTC was reestablished in 1936, providing a means whereby students completing the basic and advanced courses concurrently with their professional training could qualify for commission in the Medical Corps of the Army.[2]

Dr. McKinley's successor as dean was Dr. Walter A. Bloedorn, who held the post until his retirement in 1957. He was succeeded by Dr. John L. Parks, who served until 1972. Unlike Dr. McKinley, both Dr. Bloedorn and Dr. Parks had had a long association with the Medical School before becoming dean.

Walter Andrew Bloedorn (1886-   ) and John Lewis Parks (1908-1972) were men of commanding presence, outstanding professional attainments, marked administrative skill, and great personal charm. They hold high rank among the distinguished men who have served as deans of the School of Medicine. The thirty-three years of their tenure—Dean Bloedorn from 1939 to 1957 and Dean Parks from 1957 to 1972—saw the School of Medicine move into the larger concept of the Medical Center.

Dean Bloedorn, a native of Platte Center, Nebraska, received his degree of doctor of medicine from Creighton University in 1909, his B.A. and M.A. from George Washington, which conferred upon him the degree of doctor of science, *honoris causa*, in 1948. The early part of his professional career was spent as an officer in the Medical Corps of the United States Navy. Appointed professor of tropical medicine in the School of Medicine in 1926, he became professor of medicine in 1930, director of clinics in 1931, assistant dean in 1930, and dean from 1939 to 1957. He was also medical director of the University Hospital from 1932 to the time of his retirement. Dean Bloedorn was a fellow of the American College of Physicians and a member of the National Committee of UNESCO. A recognized authority in the field of medical education, he was a former president of the Association of American Medical Colleges and of the National Board of Medical Examiners. Upon his retirement as dean he became president of the Gorgas Memorial Institute of Tropical and Preventive Medicine. The years of his tenure as dean saw great expansion in the size of the full-time teaching staff, increasing emphasis on research, and the building, equipment, and organization of the University Hospital at Washington Circle.

Dean Bloedorn's successor was Dr. John L. Parks. A native of Muskogee, Oklahoma, he received his training at the University of Wisconsin, B.A. 1930, M.S. 1932, M.D. 1934. He came to Washington in 1938 as chief medical officer of obstetrics and gynecology in the District of Columbia General Hospital, then known as Gallinger Hospital. Six years later, he left Gallinger to become professor of obstetrics and gynecology and in 1957 dean of the School of Medicine and medical director of the University Hospital. His service as dean continued until 1972, when he became vice president for medical affairs. Like his predecessor he was a former president of the Association of American Medical Colleges and of the National Board of Medical Examiners. His distinction in his specialty brought him wide recognition both at home and abroad. Dr. Parks was a former president of the American Association of Obstetrics and Gynecology and, at the time of his death, president of the American Gynecological Society. He was a fellow of the Royal College of Obstetricians and Gynecologists and of the American College of Surgeons. In speaking of Dean Parks' achievements on the occasion of the celebration of his tenth anniversary as dean, his predecessor, Dr. Bloedorn, said of him, "His curricular revisions have attracted nation-wide interest and particular attention from other medical schools."[3]

In 1972, Dr. Parks became vice president for medical affairs. At his death shortly after his appointment to this office, Dr. James J. Feffer, Professor of Medicine, a graduate of Indiana University, became vice president for medical affairs. There was a touch of tragedy in the fact that Dr. Parks passed on just as the Medical Center was about to occupy its new quarters for which he and his associates had so long planned and labored. In his death the University and medical education lost an eloquent and influential spokesman.

In 1968 Dean Parks had prevailed upon Dr. Feffer, then clinical professor of medicine, to devote his whole time and energy as associate dean for clinical affairs to faculty recruitment and the innovation of bold new programs. It was fitting that he should succeed Dr. Parks as vice president for medical affairs. Implementing and securing financial support for the plans of these two men were the highly resourceful, energetic, and successful activities of another member of the Medical faculty, Dr. Seymour Alpert, vice president for development.[4]

While great educational progress was made under the leadership of these men and the able associates in administration whom they brought together—men like the late Angus MacIver Griffin—their major contributions were, perhaps, two in number. Each by his own prestige and by constructive activities in professional organizations, recognized by election to high offices, contributed notably to the distinction of the School he headed. Each of them devoted his considerable ability with outstanding success to developing and elaborating the intricate plans for the Medical Center at Washington Circle and marshaling the support that converted those plans into reality. It is all the more remarkable that this was being done while the nation was involved in foreign wars, declared and undeclared, in civil strife, and in vast social unrest.

Midway in the tenure of Dean Parks, the long administration of President Marvin came to a close. The next six years (1959-1965) were made up of a two-year period when Dean O. S. Colclough served as acting president, the brief administration of President Thomas Henry Carroll terminated by his death after three years of service, and a second short period when Dean Colclough again held the acting presidency. In 1965, Lloyd Hartman Elliott, then president of the University of Maine, was selected as the fourteenth president of George Washington University. He brought to his task wide educational experience, as teacher and administrator in the public schools and at the University of Colorado and at Cornell University, prior to his being called to the University of Maine. It served him in good stead as he had to face student unrest, turmoil in the city and the nation, and grave problems posed by escalating costs. Stringent measures of economy, the generosity of friends, and the support of Congressional appropriations for medical education enabled him to avoid the deficit so characteristic of educational institutions in the period.

While a discussion of educational activities, the activities of the classroom, does not fall within the province of an institutional history such as this, it is well to point out and illustrate that attention to the details of planning and to material things did not interrupt the continued improvement of the curriculum, the strengthening of the faculty, and the widening outreach of the School's services.

An examination of the schedules of classes issued each year for the guidance of students shows the degree to which the enrichment of the curriculum, the organization of the clinical department, and complete and demanding utilization of the full time of the student had progressed. To teach the courses announced, staffing both the classrooms and the laboratories, to direct research, and to provide for a highly organized clinical program required a faculty far removed in number from "the historic septenary" that Sir William Osler referred to in his days at McGill.[5]

The first integrated program of postgraduate courses offered by the Medical School was presented in 1946. This series was first planned for veterans who were physicians returning to practice and in its earlier years was made possible by a foundation grant. The first course consisted of a general review course covering most of the fields of medical practice in survey, stressing recent advances and clinical training in the specialties.[6]

The Trustees had approved the 90 semester-hour requirement for admission to the Medical School in the fall of 1940. As the war came nearer the Board approved an accelerated program and the adoption of a trimester system. In order to meet the government's desire to increase hospital facilities in the District, the University offered to put at its disposal a suitable site should it want to erect temporary quarters maintained by the University. As a war measure the entrance requirements were temporarily moved back to two years of pre-medical work. The 90 semester-hour requirement was restored in September, 1947. The use of the services of the Medical School was offered for the training of certain Army and Navy personnel.[7]

As anxious as the School of Medicine and the Hospital were to serve the government and the community in a larger way, they were stalemated by lack of space for expansion. The limited area of the University's property on H Street was entirely built up. The School of Medicine and the Hospital found themselves in a strait jacket. Relocation in the University area in the West End with vastly larger structures and equipment that was adequate for service, teaching, and research was indicated. The planning for a new University Hospital at Washington Circle indicated the area where the Medical Center was to be developed over a period of twenty-five years.

PART THREE

The Medical Center
(Washington Circle)

CHAPTER SEVENTEEN

Planning and Fulfillment

On October 20, 1943, Dr. Charles Edward Remy reported to the Federal Works Administrator on a survey he had made on the hospital situation in the metropolitan area. He referred, with approval, to the University's plan for development. On February 10, 1944, the University's plan was presented to the Park and Planning Commission and endorsed by that body two months later. It proposed a hospital of 500 to 600 beds to be built in Square 54, between 22nd and 23rd Streets, Eye Street, and Pennsylvania Avenue. Formal application for federal assistance for the construction of a new hospital was made on May 22, 1944, and approved by the Federal Works Agency and the President of the United States on September 8.

It was agreed that by an understanding between the University and the Federal Works Agency the two parties would enter into a lease arrangement for five years, effective when the property was formally delivered to the University. The government agreed to build a hospital on Square 54 and put educational facilities, fixtures, and appointments at the disposal of the University. The University obligated itself to pay the government $100,000 at the time of execution of the lease, and $250,000 if and when it took possession of the property, and in addition, to pay costs of maintenance and repair. To make these payments, the University borrowed $350,000 on the medical property on H Street.

The arrangement with the government did not provide for the equipment of the Hospital. Since these funds had to be raised privately, the Trustees authorized the solicitation of an $800,000 fund to defray these costs. Major General U. S. Grant III (Ret.) was made chairman of the hospital fund-raising committee.

This distinguished officer, grandson of the eighteenth President and a member of the Board of Trustees, had been elected vice president of the University to undertake this important assignment and to deal with the many problems arising from the development of the University plan within the capital city. In this area, no one had greater expertise. As the active head of countless agencies and groups, public and private, General Grant had had more to do with the planning of the city than any of his contemporaries.[1]

President Marvin had now lost all of his early diffidence in seeking and utilizing government aid. He was assisted not only by his own considerable ability in negotiation, by the expert advice of General Grant and the support of an influential Board of Trustees, but also by the drive, good judgment, and zeal of an exceedingly effective dean, Dr. Bloedorn.

Various facilitating measures for the needs of the Hospital and the continuance of government aid were undertaken. The equipment fund was subscribed. A new apartment house facing the Hospital was purchased as a Nurses Home. An agreement was made with the Washington Home for Foundlings for the use of the Warwick Memorial. A resolution was adopted by the Trustees, pointing out the shortage of educational facilities for training under the Servicemen's Readjustment Act, as a basis for applying to the government for facilities needed in carrying out its purposes.[2]

As early as 1944 President Marvin had formulated a plan he hoped would bring about the release of the trust on the medical property on H Street; this had been placed on that property following the Attorney General's investigation of 1910 to assure the complete restoration of endowment funds. Five years later, the president reported to the Board that the lease agreement had been so modified that, it being understood that the medical property which the University was obligated to turn over to the government had been valued at $548,167.50, the University could buy the Hospital for that sum. Crediting toward that amount the lease rental of $100,000 paid in 1945 and the payment of $250,000 in 1948 in accordance with agreements, there remained a balance of $198,167.50 on payment of which the government would turn over a quitclaim for Square 54 and all of its improvements. The president's intricate arrangements for the release of the trust on the H Street holdings were carried out and the University was able to certify to the Attorney General that the endowment funds were completely restored. By expert negotiations and ingenuity, the University held the new Hospital property in fee

graphic laboratories, medical illustration, and audiovisual support services for teaching.[9]

Not only had all of the units of the Medical Center been brought together, but also, for the first time in more than sixty years, all of the activities of the University had been brought together in a great University Center. It was a memorable achievement.

The University had not entered into the formation of its Medical Center with precipitate speed. Planning during the administration of three presidents, herculean efforts on the part of three deans—Bloedorn, Parks, and Feffer—the work of numerous committees, individuals, and consultants had all entailed a long and detailed undertaking. Elaborate research, much of it supported by foundations and published because of its contribution to the problems of a medical center, was carried on. A significant example was a report from the George Washington University School of Medicine Facilities Study, directed by Dr. Thomas M. Peery, and published by the University in February, 1965, under the title *Design for Medical Education: The Development and Planning of a Medical College and Care Center.* This report, says the Foreword, "describes the steps one medical school has taken to translate its educational objectives, philosophy, and techniques into laboratory, classroom, and clinic."

The physical plant of the Medical Center as planned and built was designed to make possible the mobilization of the total medical resources of the University to meet fully the demands for service, training, and research. The educational program of the School of Medicine had gone far beyond the simple curriculum, upon the successful completion of which the M.D. degree was rewarded. Students in cooperation with the undergraduate College of Arts and Science could follow a seven-year curriculum leading to the combined degrees of Bachelor of Arts and Doctor of Medicine; or, in cooperation with the Graduate School of Arts and Sciences, they could take a program leading to the combined degrees of Master of Science and Doctor of Medicine, or a dual degree program for those seeking both the Doctor of Medicine and the Doctor of Philosophy degree in certain fields. In addition, students could take either the Master of Science or the Doctor of Philosophy degree in the Graduate School of Arts and Sciences. The Medical Center was designed to meet fully the heavy demand on research which such an extensive program implied.

The enlarged University Hospital and the University Clinic offered medical service in accord not only with the highest standards of medical care but as well with the obligations imposed by the socioeconomic demands of a great metropolitan community.

The School of Medicine was established, when the nation was less than fifty years old, in the small capital city where the government had been located for but a quarter of a century. Only ten existing American medical schools antedate it in origin. For almost fifty years it endured through the precarious existence of a purely proprietary school. In the next half-century it slowly emerged from its proprietary status, step by step, into a full fiscal and organic relation to the University. Then there was another fifty years of planning, organizing resources, and evolving a distinguished educational plan and program of research; and, finally, the completion of the Medical Center.

Its exodus had ended, but all of this had been only prologue. The promised land lay ahead, and in a new setting its history was yet to be written.

"The past is prologue."

GENERAL BIBLIOGRAPHICAL NOTE

The prime sources for a study of the institutional development of medical education in the University are two in number: the *Minutes of the Board of Trustees* and the so-called *Dean's Book*, Vol. 1, 1839–1880, and Vol. 2, 1880–1904. The *Minutes* have been preserved, without a break, from the organization meeting in 1821 to the present. During the long period when the Medical Department was proprietary in character, its concerns came to the attention of the Trustees in only a formal fashion, principally for the conferring of the mandamus for granting degrees and for the confirmation of nominations of faculty members. The Medical faculty, in a fashion, was its own board of trustees as well as a body of teachers. While the first ten years of operation are not covered, beginning with the reorganization of 1839 the *Dean's Book* gives a detailed account of the School's complete activities down through the beginning of the present century. By that time the Medical School had become sufficiently integrated with the University structure so that the records of the Trustees offer relatively full information concerning it.

Second in importance are the circulars of earlier days, and the annual catalogues. The run of circulars is not complete and the degree of incompleteness is impossible to determine. Some are not dated and apparently a supply was printed at times to last for more than a single year.

To these must be added the *Annual Reports of the President*, the *Annual Reports of the University Hospital*, the *Annual Reports of the Dean*, the student yearbooks of the University and of the Medical School, the University student papers, and the news publications of the medical alumni and of the Hospital. The University archives contain the accumulation of a century and a half of records. A large collection of pamphlet material, particularly in the Wright collection, includes Commencement addresses, inaugural lectures, addresses on special occasions, and numerous miscellaneous publications.

Complete citations where used are given in the Notes which follow for each chapter.

BIBLIOGRAPHICAL COMMENTS ON CHAPTERS 1 TO 3

For the history of the University, Elmer Louis Kayser, *Bricks Without Straw* (Appleton-Century-Crofts, 1970) and the materials referred to in that book have been used.

No full-length study of the history of the School of Medicine has previously been written. There are several historical sketches of considerable value, some of which have been included in larger publications. Among these are: Robert W. Prichard, *Historical Sketch of the Medical School of the George Washington University* (Washington, 1947); *The Golden Book of the George Washington University Hospital* (Washington, 1949); A. Barnes Hooe, "Annual Address of the President of the George Washington University Medical Society," *The George Washington University Bulletin,* Vol. 5, No. 3, pp. 78-84.

For background material on the early history of the District of Columbia, in addition to the local newspapers, there are the two large works: Wilhelmus Bogart Bryan, *A History of the National Capital from Its Foundation Through the Period of the Adoption of the Organic Act,* 2 vols. (New York, 1914-1916); and Constance McLaughlin Green, *Washington, Village and Capital, 1800-1879* (Princeton, 1962), and *Washington, Capital City, 1878-1950* (Princeton, 1963). The classical description of the city's coming into being is Christian Hines, *Early Recollections of Washington City* (Washington, 1866), an account of the way the city appeared to the author, 1796-1814. Of the many other contemporary works containing much descriptive material, among the most useful are Jonathan Elliot, *Historical Sketches of Ten Miles Square Forming the District of Columbia, with a Picture of Washington, etc.,* (Washington, 1830); David Bailie Warden, *A Chorographical and Statistical Description of the District of Columbia, the Seat of the General Government of the United States,* with an engraved plan of the District, and view of the Capitol (Paris, 1816); Samuel C. Busey, *Pictures of the City of Washington in the Past* (Washington, 1898).

For the early history of the medical profession, its institutions, and its members in the District of Columbia, first mention must be given to Joseph Toner, *Anniversary Oration Delivered Before the Medical Society of the District of Columbia, September 22, 1866* (Washington, 1869), and to the *History of the Medical Society of the District of Columbia, 1817-1909, Part II, 1833-1944,* 2 vols. (Washington, 1909, 1947). Of value are the writings of Samuel Clagett Busey, particularly his *Personal Reminiscences and Recollections of Forty-six Years' Membership in the Medical Society of the District of Columbia, and Residence in This City, with Biographical Sketches of Many of the Deceased Members* (Washington, 1895), and *A Souvenir with an Autobiographical Sketch of Early Life and Selected Miscellaneous Addresses and Communications* (Washington, 1896).

Of the many directories of alumni which have appeared from time to time (the latest medical alumni directory was published in 1968), the most useful historically is *The Columbian University Historical Catalogue, 1821-1891* (Washington, 1891), compiled by Howard Lincoln Hodgkins, containing not only a historical sketch of the University, but many biographical details about members of the faculty and graduates.

A great wealth of detail will be found in the many papers published in the *Records of the Columbia Historical Society*, Vols. 1-   (Washington, 1895-   ) and in the *Medical Annals of the District of Columbia*. Although very uneven in quality and often journalistic in tone, much of value will be found in *Washington, Past and Present: A History*, edited by John Clagett Proctor (New York, 1930), Vol. 2, containing chapters by many different authors.

Notes, Chapter 1

[1] David B. Warden, *A Chorographical and Statistical Description of the District of Columbia* (Paris, 1816), p. 33.

[2] *Ibid.*, p. 32.

[3] Christian Hines, *Early Recollections of Washington City* (Washington, 1866), pp. 31, 35, 44.

[4] Allen C. Clark, *Greenleaf and Law in the Federal City* (Washington, 1901), pp. 140-143.

[5] Hines, *op. cit.*, pp. 6, 7, 18, 19, 30, 31.

[6] Warden, *op. cit.*, pp. 16, 17.

[7] *Ibid.*, pp. 92, 126; J. W. Toner, *Anniversary Oration Delivered Before the Medical Society of the District of Columbia, September 26, 1866* (Washington, 1869), pp. 5, 6.

[8] Warden, *op. cit.*, p. 97.

[9] Toner, *op. cit.*, pp. 6, 7.

[10] *Ibid.*, pp. 6-10; *History of the Medical Society of the District of Columbia, 1817-1909* (Washington, 1909), pp. 2-5.

[11] *Ibid.*, pp. 5-8.

[12] Toner, *op. cit.*, p. 14.

Notes, Chapter 2

[1] *Stat. at Large*, Vol. 6, pp. 255-258, 16th Cong., 2nd Sess., Chap. 10, Secs. 1, 7.

[2] Elmer Louis Kayser, *Bricks Without Straw, The Evolution of George Washington University* (New York, 1970), pp. 27-37.

[3] *Ibid.*, pp. 50, 51.

[4] *Minutes of the Board of Trustees*, Vol. 1 (December 30, 1822).

[5] Kayser, *op. cit.*, p. 47.

[6] Constance McLaughlin Green, *Washington, Village and Capital, 1800-1878* (Princeton, 1962), p. 69.

[7] Kayser, *op. cit.*, pp. 47, 148, 149.

[8] *Ibid.*, pp. 47, 48.

[9] *Circular of the Medical Department of Columbian College, Washington, D.C.* (Washington, 1843), pp. 3, 4.

[10] Thomas Sewall, M.D., *A Lecture Delivered at the Opening of the Medical Department of the Columbian College in the District of Columbia, March 30, 1825* (Washington City, 1825).

11 J. W. Toner, *Anniversary Oration Delivered Before the Medical Society of the District of Columbia, September 26, 1866* (Washington, 1869), p. 47.

12 Henry Sewall Webster, *Thomas Sewall, Some of His Ancesters, and All of His Descendents: A Genealogy* (Gardiner, Maine, 1904), pp. 3-6, 15.

13 Arthur Marvel Lassek, *Human Dissection, Its Drama and Struggle* (Springfield, Illinois, 1958), pp. 186-190.

14 *History of the Medical Society of the District of Columbia, 1817-1900* (Washington, 1909), p. 222.

15 Howard Lincoln Hodgkins (comp.), *Historical Catalogue of the Officers and Graduates of the Columbian University, Washington, D.C., 1821-1891* (Washington, 1891), p. 103.

16 *Minutes of the Board of Trustees*, Vol. 1 (April 11, 1827), p. 216; S. W. Lynd, *Memoir of the Reverend William Staughton, D.D.* (Boston, 1834), pp. 209, 210, 268-271; Thomas Sewall, M.D., *A Charge Delivered to the Graduating Class of The Columbian College at the Medical Commencement, March 22, 1827* (Washington, 1828).

17 J. C. Furnas, *The Life and Times of the Late Demon Rum* (New York, 1905), pp. 57, 58.

18 Thomas Sewall, M.D., *An Address Delivered Before the Washington City Temperance Society, November 15, 1830* (Washington, 1830).

19 Ernest Hurst Cherrington (ed.), *Standard Encyclopedia of the Alcohol Problem* (Westerville, Ohio, 1925), Vol. 1, chart facing p. 110, p. 289; *ibid.*, 1929, Vol. 5, p. 2424; Furnas, *op. cit.*, p. 57; Fielding H. Garrison, *An Introduction to the History of Medicine, Fourth Edition* (Philadelphia, 1960), pp. 476, 477.

20 Lynd, *op. cit.*, pp. 233 ff.; *Columbian Star*, April 28, 1826, "Letter to the Superintending Committee."

21 *History of the Medical Society*, p. 224.

22 Lynd, *op. cit.*, following p. 311: "Note which ought to have been inserted in page 32"; Letter from Elbert Staughton Wade to Dr. Seymour Alpert, May 31, 1971.

23 Samuel C. Busey, *Personal Reminiscences and Recollections of Forty-six Years' Membership in the Medical Society of the District of Columbia, and Residence in This City, with Biographical Sketches of Many of the Deceased Members* (Washington, 1895), pp. 135-137; *History of the Medical Society*, pp. 148, 214-215; Hodgkins, *op. cit.*, p. 50.

24 *History of the Medical Society*, pp. 148, 217, 218.

25 *Ibid.*, p. 148.

26 Hodgkins, op. cit., pp. 48-52; *History of the Medical Society*, pp. 148, 218; Busey, *op. cit.*, pp. 24, 25.

27 *History of the Medical Society*, pp. 147-150; Hodgkins, *op. cit.*, p. 85.

Notes, Chapter 3

1 Elmer Louis Kayser, *Bricks Without Straw, The Evolution of George Washington University* (New York, 1970), pp. 56-79.

2 Elmer Louis Kayser, *Luther Rice, Founder of Columbian College* (Washington, 1966), pp. 18-24.

3 *History of the Medical Society of the District of Columbia, 1817-1909* (Washington, 1909), pp. 9-13; J. W. Toner, *Anniversary Oration Delivered Before the Medical Society of the District of Columbia, September 26, 1866* (Washington, 1869), p. 18.

⁴ Samuel C. Busey, *Personal Reminiscences and Recollections of Forty-six Years' Membership in the Medical Society of the District of Columbia, and Residence in This City, with Biographical Sketches of Many of the Deceased Members* (Washington, 1895), p. 103; Toner, *op. cit.*, p. 22.

⁵ *History of the Medical Society*, pp. 5, 6, 7, 11, 12, 13.

⁶ Toner, *op. cit.*, pp. 25-28.

⁷ Georgetown (D.C.) *Metropolitan*, Vol. 6 (March 25, 1826), p. 2, cols. 1, 2.

⁸ *Minutes of the Board of Trustees*, Vol. 2 (April 27, 1836), pp. 14, 15.

⁹ Howard Lincoln Hodgkins (comp.), *Historical Catalogue of the Officers and Graduates of the Columbian University, Washington, D.C., 1821-1891* (Washington, 1891), pp. 48-57, 103-105; Toner, *op. cit.*, p. 47; *Minutes of the Board of Trustees*, Vol. 1 (October 3, 1834), p. 347.

¹⁰ *Washington City Chronicle*, January 31, 1829, p. 3, col. 2; *The Globe*, Vol. 2, No. 89 (September 25, 1832), p. 3, col. 4.

¹¹ *Columbian Gazette*, Vol. 1 (October 31, 1829), p. 3, col. 1.

¹² *The Globe*, Vol. 1, No. 156 (December 13, 1829), p. 1, col. 6.

¹³ *Ibid.*, Vol. 3, No. 123 (November 4, 1833), p. 1, col. 5.

¹⁴ Wyndham D. Wiles, "Chemist Jones, Superintendent of the Patent Office," "Public Lectures in Chemistry in the United States," *AMBIX*, Vol. 15, No. 3 (October, 1968), pp. 138-139.

BIBLIOGRAPHICAL COMMENT ON CHAPTERS 4 TO 12

Beginning with Chapter 4, the *Dean's Book*, Vols. 1 and 2, becomes an invaluable guide for the next nine chapters. More than the usual *Minutes* of a faculty, these volumes recording the business of monthly and special meetings deal with matters administrative and financial as well as educational. With the *Minutes of the Board of Trustees* giving the larger institutional setting and supplemented by the annual catalogues, circulars, and special announcements, the *Dean's Book* gives not only the skeleton, but a well-filled-out skeleton for the narrative of the long middle period.

Notes, Chapter 4

¹ See, for example, in *Dean's Book*, Vol. 1 (September 2, 1845), his demands as to the location of his signature on the diplomas.

² *History of the Medical Society of the District of Columbia, 1817-1909* (Washington, 1909), pp. 225, 226; Samuel C. Busey, *Personal Reminiscences and Recollections of Forty-six Years' Membership in the Medical Society of the District of Columbia, and Residence in This City, with Biographical Sketches of Many of the Deceased Members* (Washington, 1895), pp. 155, 156. Busey first knew Dr. Lindsly as his teacher in the Medical Department of Columbian.

³ *History of the Medical Society*, pp. 226, 227; Howard Lincoln Hodgkins (comp.), *Historical Catalogue of the Officers and Graduates of the Columbian University, Washington, D.C., 1821-1891* (Washington, 1891), p. 48; Wilhemus Bogart Bryan, *A History of the National Capital* (New York, 1916), Vol. 2, p. 339.

⁴ Busey, *op. cit.*, pp. 169-174.

5 *Ibid.*, p. 24; Hodgkins, *op. cit.*, pp. 48-51; *History of the Medical Society*, p. 229; Virginia Miller, "Doctor Thomas Miller and His Times," *Records of the Columbia Historical Society Washington, 1900*, Vol. 3, pp. 303-323.

6 *History of the Medical Society*, pp. 229, 230; Hodgkins, *op. cit.*, pp. 48-57; Elmer Louis Kayser, *Bricks Without Straw, The Evolution of George Washington University* (New York, 1970), pp. 125-126.

7 Busey, *op. cit.*, pp. 158, 159.

8 *The Globe*, Vol. 9, No. 123 (November 4, 1839), p. 2, col. 6.

9 *Dean's Book*, Vol. 1, pp. 1, 2, 3; *Minutes of the Board of Trustees*, Vol. 2 (July 29, 1839), p. 44.

10 *Dean's Book*, Vol. 1 (June ?, 1839); *ibid.*, Vol. 1 (July ?, 1839); *ibid.*, Vol. 1 (August ?, 16, 1839); *ibid.*, Vol. 1 (September 28, 1839).

11 *Ibid.*, Vol. 1 (April ?, 1840); *ibid.*, Vol. 1 (July 8, 1840); *ibid.*, Vol. 1 (August 4, 14, 1840); *ibid.*, Vol. 1 (October 6, 18, 28, 1840).

12 *Ibid.*, Vol. 1 (September 28, 1839).

13 *Ibid.*, Vol. 1 (February 15, 28, 1844).

14 *Ibid.*, Vol. 1 (October 23, 1841; *ibid.*, Vol. 1 (November 24, 1841).

15 *Ibid.*, Vol. 1 (November 5, 1842).

16 *Ibid.*, Vol. 1 (July 13, 1844).

17 *Ibid.*, Vol. 1 (February 1, 15, 1844).

18 *Ibid.*, Vol. 1 (November 17, 1843).

19 *Ibid.*, Vol. 1 (November 3, 1843); *ibid.*, Vol. 1 (July 13, 1844).

20 *Ibid.*, Vol. 1 (February 1, 1844).

21 *Ibid.*, Vol. 1 (October 21, 1844).

22 William Frederick Norwood, "Medical Education in the United States Before 1900," in C. D. O'Malley (ed.), *The History of Medical Education*, U.C.L.A. Forum Med. Sc., No. 12 (Los Angeles, 1970), p. 475.

23 *Dean's Book*, Vol. 1 (August 23, 1843); *ibid.*, Vol. 1 (October 31, 1843); *ibid.*, Vol. 1 (November 17, 1843); *ibid.*, Vol. 1 (February 15, 1844).

24 *Ibid.*, Vol. 1 (April 1, 1841).

25 *Ibid.*, Vol. 1 (March 17, 1843).

26 *Ibid.*, Vol. 1 (June 18, 20, 1844); *ibid.*, Vol. 1 (July 1, 13, 1844).

27 Coleman Nevils, *Miniatures of Georgetown, 1634 to 1934: Tercentennial Causeries* (Washington).

Notes, Chapter 5

1 J. W. Toner, *Anniversary Oration Delivered Before the Medical Society of the District of Columbia, September 26, 1866* (Washington, 1869), pp. 55-75; Wilhemus Bogart Bryan, *A History of the National Capital* (New York, 1916), Vol. 2, pp. 338-341; Constance McLaughlin Green, *Washington, Village and Capital, 1800-1878* (Princeton, 1962), p. 165.

2 *The Globe*, July 27, 1844.

3 Gerald B. Webb and Desmond Powell, *Henry Sewall, Physiologist and Physician* (Baltimore, 1946), p. 2.

4 Sister Bernadette Arminger, R.N., Daughter of Charity of St. Vincent de Paul, *The History of the Hospital Work of the Daughters of Charity of Vincent de Paul in the Eastern Province of the United States, 1832-1860* (typescript 1949); *Dean's Book*, minutes of meetings from March 12, 1845, to April 3, 1846.

5 *Ibid.*, Vol. 1 (November 6, 1845).

⁶ *Ibid.*, Vol. 1 (August 24, 1848).

⁷ Samuel C. Busey, *Personal Reminiscences and Recollections of Forty-six Years' Membership in the Medical Society of the District of Columbia, and Residence in This City, with Biographical Sketches of Many of the Deceased Members* (Washington, 1895), p. 215.

⁸ Bryan, *op. cit.*, Vol. 2, p. 341.

⁹ Joseph Thomas Durkin, S.J., *Georgetown University: The Middle Years (1840-1900)* (Washington, 1963), p. 29; Coleman Nevils, *Miniatures of Georgetown, 1634 to 1934, Tercentennial Causeries* (Washington), p. 202. (Father Nevils adds a fourth name of the founders, that of Dr. Charles H. Liebermann.) James S. Easby-Smith, *Georgetown University in the District of Columbia, 1789-1907* (New York, 1907), pp. 313 ff.

¹⁰ *Dean's Book*, Vol. 1, November 1, 27, 1847); *ibid.*, Vol. 1 (August 24, 1848); *ibid.*, Vol. 1 (February ?, 1849).

¹¹ *Ibid.*, Vol. 1 (February ?, 1849).

¹² *Ibid.*, Vol. 1 (June 7, 1849); *ibid.*, Vol. 1 (December 15, 1849); *ibid.*, Vol. 1 (May 1, 1850).

¹³ *Ibid.*, Vol. 1 (June 7, 1849); *ibid.*, Vol. 1 (December 15, 1849); *ibid.*, Vol. 1 (May 1, 1850); *ibid.*, Vol. 1 (September 12, 1854); *ibid.*, Vol. 1 (December 23, 1854).

¹⁴ *Ibid.*, Vol. 1 (November 8, 1856).

¹⁵ *Ibid.*, Vol. 1 (May 2, 1857); *ibid.*, Vol. 1 (December 6, 1857).

¹⁶ *Ibid.*, Vol. 1 (February 5, 1858).

¹⁷ *Ibid.*, Vol. 1 (May ?, 1848).

¹⁸ *Ibid.*, Vol. 1 (May 29, 1857).

¹⁹ *Ibid.*, Vol. 1 (May 27, 1857); *ibid.*, Vol. 1 (September 13, 1858).

²⁰ *Ibid.*, Vol. 1 (October 5, 1855). For later phases of the problem, see Elmer Louis Kayser, *Bricks Without Straw, The Evolution of George Washington University* (New York, 1970), pp. 165-167, 215.

²¹ *Dean's Book*, Vol. 1 (June 28, 1848); *ibid.*, Vol. 1 (February 13, 1849).

²² Toner, *op. cit.*, pp. 55-57; *Washington News*, November 13, 1853, p. 2, col. 2; *ibid.*, January 21, 1854, p. 2, col. 2.

²³ *Dean's Book*, Vol. 1 (May 16, 1854); *ibid.*, Vol. 1 (May 29, 1857).

²⁴ *Ibid.*, Vol. 1 (April 30, 1849).

²⁵ *Ibid.*, Vol. 1 (May 3, 1860).

²⁶ *Ibid.*, Vol. 1 (December 7, 1860).

²⁷ *Washington News*, July 14, 1855, col. 3.

²⁸ *Dean's Book*, Vol. 1 (May 10, 1857).

²⁹ Toner, *op. cit.*, p. 57.

³⁰ John Wells Bulkley, *The War Hospitals*, n.d., n.p., pp. 148-149, in Washington Collection, D.C. Public Library. Source not indicated.

³¹ *Dean's Book*, Vol. 1 (October 18, 1861).

³² *Ibid.*, Vol. 1 (July 20, 1863); *ibid.*, Vol. 1 (November 7, 1863).

³³ *Ibid.*, Vol. 1 (July 27, 1863); *Minutes of the Board of Trustees*, Vol. 3 (June 28, 1864), pp. 116 ff.

³⁴ Howard Lincoln Hodgkins (comp.), *Historical Catalogue of the Officers and Graduates of the Columbian University, Washington, D.C., 1821-1891* (Washington, 1891), pp. 48, 49, 52, 107, 112; for service record of M. K. Moxley, see National Archives, RG 94, Container 542; *History of the Medical Society of the District of Columbia, 1817-1909* (Washington, 1909), p. 238.

³⁵ Horace Herndon Cunningham, *Doctors in Gray: The Confederate Medical*

Service (Baton Rouge, 1958), pp. 269, 270; Hodgkins, *op. cit.*, pp. 48, 52; *History of the Medical Society*, p. 244; Busey, *op. cit.*, pp. 192-196.

36 Hodgkins, *op. cit.*, pp. 48, 49, 50.

37 James Alonzo Bishop, *The Day Lincoln Was Shot* (New York, 1955), pp. 215-217; Hodgkins, *op. cit.*, pp. 87, 111; Kayser, *Bricks Without Straw*, pp. 125-126.

38 Worth B. Daniels, "Albert Freeman Africanus King (1841-1915): His Theory as to the Transmission of Malaria by Mosquitos," *Medical Annals of the District of Columbia*, Vol. 19, No. 9 (September, 1950), pp. 499-506.

Notes, Chapter 6

1 For details, see Elmer Louis Kayser, *Bricks Without Straw, The Evolution of George Washington University* (New York, 1970), chap. 11.

2 *Dean's Book*, Vol. 1 (October 18, 1861).

3 J. W. Toner, *Anniversary Oration Delivered Before the Medical Society of the District of Columbia, September 26, 1866* (Washington, 1869), p. 47.

4 *Sunday Morning Chronicle*, March 9, 1862, p. 3, col. 2.

5 *Ibid.*, June 29, 1862, p. 1, col. 2; *Minutes of the Board of Trustees*, Vol. 3 (June 23, 1863), pp. 97 ff.; Toner, *op. cit.*, p. 38.

6 *Minutes of the Board of Trustees*, Vol. 3 (June 24, 1862), pp. 74 ff.

7 House of Representatives, 61st Cong., 3rd Sess., Doc. 1060, p. 84.

8 Federal Writers' Project, W.P.A., American Guide Series, *Washington, City and Capital* (Washington, 1937), p. 875.

9 Quoted in *History of the Medical Society of the District of Columbia, 1817-1909* (Washington, 1909), p. 270.

10 *Minutes of the Board of Trustees*, Vol. 3 (July 12, 1865), p. 150; *Dean's Book*, Vol. 1 (July 29, 1865).

11 *Minutes of the Board of Trustees*, Vol. 3 (January 1, 1866), p. 159; *ibid.*, Vol. 3 (June 25, 1866), p. 168.

12 *Ibid.*, Vol. 3 (March 5, 1872), p. 320.

13 *The Georgetown Courier*, January 27, 1866, p. 2.

14 *Dean's Book*, Vol. 1 (October 31, 1866).

Notes, Chapter 7

1 *Dean's Book*, Vol. 1 (October 25, 27, 30, 31, 1866).

2 *Ibid.*, Vol. 1 (December 4, 1866).

3 *Ibid.*, Vol. 1 (December 17, 1866).

4 *Ibid.*, Vol. 1 (October 25, 1866); *ibid.*, Vol. 1 (December 4, 17, 1866)

5 *Ibid.*, Vol. 1 (October 9, 1867); *ibid.*, Vol. 1 (November ?, 1867); *ibid.*, Vol. 1 (March 6, 1868).

6 *Minutes of the Board of Trustees*, Vol. 3 (May 15, 1868), p. 223.

7 *Dean's Book*, Vol. 1 (February 22, 1868).

8 *The Evening Express*, August 24, 1868, p. 4, col. 2.

9 *Minutes of the Board of Trustees*, Vol. 3 (July 8, 1868), p. 232; *ibid.*, Vol. 3 (January 13, 1869), p. 235; *Dean's Book*, Vol. 1 (December 5, 1868).

10 *Ibid.*, Vol. 1 (October 6, 1868); *ibid.*, Vol. 1 (December 5, 1868); *ibid.*, Vol. 1 (March 9, 1869).

[11] *National Intelligencer,* January 11, 1869, p. 3; *Dean's Book,* Vol. 1 (January 18, 1869).

[12] *Ibid.,* Vol. 1 (March 22, 1869); *ibid.,* Vol. 1 (March 7, 1870).

[13] *Ibid.,* Vol. 1 (March 9, 1869).

[14] William E. Ames, *A History of the* National Intelligencer (Chapel Hill, 1972), pp. 306, 307, 325, 326.

[15] *Minutes of the Board of Trustees,* Vol. 3 (December 15, 1880), pp. 586, 587.

[16] *Dean's Book,* Vol. 1 (May 8, 1873); *ibid.,* Vol. 1 (March 9, 1874).

[17] *Minutes of the Board of Trustees,* Vol. 3 (March 16, 1881), p. 589.

[18] *Ibid.,* Vol. 3 (June 8, 1881), pp. 592, 593.

[19] *Dean's Book,* Vol. 2 (November 12, 1880), pp. 9, 27, 41, 55, 67.

[20] *Ibid.,* Vol. 1 (October 28, 1870).

[21] *Ibid.,* Vol. 1 (April 20, 1874); *ibid.,* Vol. 1 (August 10, 1874).

[22] *Ibid.,* Vol. 1 (March 12, 1875).

[23] *Ibid.,* Vol. 1 (August 10, 1874); *ibid.,* Vol. 1 (October 15, 1874).

Notes, Chapter 8

[1] *Dean's Book,* Vol. 1 (May 8, 1873); *ibid.,* Vol. 1 (May 24, 1877).

[2] *Ibid.,* Vol. 1 (April 26, 1880).

[3] *Ibid.,* Vol. 1 (July 11, 1879); *Catalogue of the Officers and Students of the Columbian University, for the Academic Year 1879-'80* (Washington, 1880), pp. 32, 33.

[4] C. D. O'Malley (ed.), *The History of Medical Education,* U.C.L.A. Forum Med. Sc., No. 12 (Los Angeles, 1970), pp. 487-488.

[5] Samuel C. Busey, *Personal Reminiscences and Recollections of Forty-six Years' Membership in the Medical Society of the District of Columbia, and Residence in This City, with Biographical Sketches of Many of the Deceased Members* (Washington, 1895), pp. 178-180; *History of the Medical Society of the District of Columbia, 1817-1909* (Washington, 1909), pp. 231-232.

[6] Busey, *op. cit.,* pp. 183-186; Howard Lincoln Hodgkins (comp.), *Historical Catalogue of the Officers and Graduates of the Columbian University, Washington, D.C., 1821-1891* (Washington, 1891), p. 112; *History of the Medical Society,* p. 280.

[7] *Dean's Book,* Vol. 1 (February 24, 1879); *History of the Medical Society,* p. 247; Hodgkins, *op. cit.,* p. 108.

Notes, Chapter 9

[1] *Dean's Book,* Vol. 2 (April 19, 1881), pp. 10-12; *ibid.,* Vol. 2 (January 30, 1882), p. 19; *ibid.,* Vol. 2 (March 17, 1883), p. 41; *ibid.,* Vol. 2 (March 18, 1884), p. 53.

[2] *Ibid.,* Vol. 2 (April 21, 1881), p. 14.

[3] *Ibid.,* Vol. 2 (March 20, 1886), p. 76.

[4] *Ibid.,* Vol. 2 (March 20, 1886), pp. 18, 30.

[5] *Ibid.,* Vol. 2 (March 18, 1884), p. 54; *ibid.,* Vol. 2 (December 22, 1884), pp. 60-62; Elmer Louis Kayser, *Bricks Without Straw, The Evolution of George Washington University* (New York, 1970), pp. 142-143, 150, 165-167.

[6] *Dean's Book,* Vol. 2 (March 21, 1887), p. 87; *ibid.,* Vol. 2 (March 31, 1887), p. 90; Elliott Coues, *A Woman in the Case,* An Address, Delivered at the Annual Com-

mencement of the National Medical College, in the Congregational Church of Washington, March 16, 1887 (Washington, 1887), pp. 3-7, 9-12, 19-23, 32.

7 Wyndham D. Miles, *Edward T. Fristoe: From Confederate Colonel to President of the Chemical Society of Washington*, 1969 (typescript).

8 *Dean's Book*, Vol. 1 (March 14, 25, 1878).

9 *Ibid.*, Vol. 2 (March 19, 1881).

10 *Ibid.*, Vol. 2 (October 10, 1887), p. 95.

11 *Ibid.*, Vol. 2 (March 6-8, 1888), p. 109.

12 *Ibid.*, Vol. 2 (February 1, 1886), p. 70; *ibid.*, Vol. 2 (October 7, 1886), p. 79.

13 *Ibid.*, Vol. 2 (March 20, 1886), p. 75.

14 *Ibid.*, Vol. 2 (March 31, 1887), pp. 88, 89.

15 *Ibid.*, Vol. 2 (May 1, 1886), p. 77; *ibid.*, Vol. 2 (March 31, 1887), p. 88.

16 *Ibid.*, Vol. 2 (March 21, 1887), p. 86; *ibid.*, Vol. 2 (April 19, 1887), p. 92; *ibid.*, Vol. 2 (October 4, 1887), p. 95.

17 *Ibid.*, Vol. 2 (November 7, 1887), pp. 101, 102.

18 *Ibid.*, Vol. 2 (May 31, 1887), p. 89; *ibid.*, Vol. 2 (September 24, 1888), p. 120; *ibid.*, Vol. 2 (September 29, 1888), p. 123.

19 *Ibid.*, Vol. 2 (March 21, 1887), p. 86; *ibid.*, Vol. 2 (October 4, 1887), p. 95.

Notes, Chapter 10

1 *Dean's Book*, Vol. 2 (January 23, 1883), p. 36; *ibid.*, Vol. 2 (September 15, 1884), p. 58; *ibid.*, Vol. 2 (April 7, 1887), p. 91; *ibid.*, Vol. 2 (May 18, 1887), p. 96.

2 *Minutes of the Board of Trustees*, Vol. 4 (June 13, 1887), p. 200; *Dean's Book*, Vol. 2 (October 4, 1887), p. 93; *ibid.*, Vol. 2 (October 20, 1887), pp. 98, 99; *ibid.*, Vol. 2 (December 27, 1887), p. 105.

3 *Ibid.*, Vol. 2 (December 27, 1887), pp. 105-108.

4 *Minutes of the Board of Trustees*, Vol. 5 (November 27, 1897), pp. 245-248.

Notes, Chapter 11

1 *Dean's Book*, Vol. 2 (November 7, 1887), p. 103.

2 *Ibid.*, Vol. 2 (October 20, 1887), p. 97.

3 *Ibid.*, Vol. 2 (September 24, 1888), p. 122.

4 *Minutes of the Board of Trustees*, Vol. 4 (June 1, 1892), p. 386; *ibid.*, Vol. 4 (June 10, 1892), pp. 389-391; *Dean's Book*, Vol. 2 (March 22, 1892), pp. 168-169; *ibid.*, Vol. 2 (April 23, 1892), pp. 170-171; *ibid.*, Vol. 2 (April 30, 1892), pp. 175, 176; *ibid.*, Vol. 2 (July 25, 1892), p. 177.

5 Elmer Louis Kayser, *Bricks Without Straw, The Evolution of George Washington University* (New York, 1970), p. 215; *Minutes of the Board of Trustees*, Vol. 7 (June 1, 1911), p. 118; *ibid.*, Vol. 7 (June 16, 1911), p. 125; *ibid.*, Vol. 7 (October 11, 1911), pp. 128, 129.

6 *Dean's Book*, Vol. 2 (November 29, 1892), pp. 181 ff.; *ibid.*, Vol. 2 (April 11, 1893), p. 187; *ibid.*, Vol. 2 (May 6, 1893), p. 197; *ibid.*, Vol. 2 (March 12, 1895), p. 229.

7 *Ibid.*, Vol. 2 (November 29, 1892), p. 181; *ibid.*, Vol. 2 (November 28, 1894), pp. 226-227.

8 *Ibid.*, Vol. 2 (September 3, 1893), pp. 203-205.

9 *Ibid.*, Vol. 2 (May 6, 1894), p. 223; *ibid.*, Vol. 2 (January 16, 1895), p. 228.

[10] *Ibid.*, Vol. 2 (July 31, 1893), pp. 199, 200.

[11] *Dean's Book*, Vol. 2 (March 17, 1892), p. 164.

Albaugh's, opened in 1884, was on the south side of Pennsylvania Avenue near 15th Street and was built above the Washington Light Infantry Armory. It was later known as Allen's Grand Opera House, then as Kernan's, next as Chase's Polite Vaudeville, and, up to the time it was demolished, as Poli's.

[12] At the Commencement of 1892 music was furnished, as it had been on a majority of such occasions, by the United States Marine Band, conducted by a "Mr. Smith," and not by John Philip Sousa, who had appeared at previous Commencements, because he had resigned in 1892 as the leader. The connection of this famous musical organization with Columbian Commencements was of long standing. Colonel Archibald Henderson, perhaps the most famous and certainly the most picturesque of Marine Commandants, was a member of the board of visitors of Washington Infirmary, and his brother, Thomas Henderson, M.D., was professor of the theory and practice of medicine from 1824 to 1833.

[13] Kayser, *Bricks Without Straw*, pp. 147-150.

[14] *Dean's Book*, Vol. 2 (February 15, 1892), pp. 183 ff.

[15] *Ibid.*, Vol. 2 (May 6, 1894), pp. 221-224.

[16] *Ibid.*, Vol. 2 (September 6, 1894), pp. 218, 219.

[17] *Ibid.*, Vol. 2 (March 12, 1895), p. 230.

[18] *Ibid.*, Vol. 2 (April 6, 1895), p. 231.

[19] *Ibid.*, Vol. 2 (April 6, 1895), p. 232; *ibid.*, Vol. 2 (April 20, 1895), pp. 233, 234.

[20] *Ibid.*, Vol. 2 (June 19, 1895), p. 240.

[21] *Ibid.*, Vol. 2 (June 19, 1895), p. 240.

[22] *Ibid.*, Vol. 2 (February 24, 1896), p. 251.

[23] Kayser, *Bricks Without Straw*, p. 179.

[24] *Dean's Book*, Vol. 2 (June 25, 1895), pp. 234-246.

[25] *Ibid.*, Vol. 2 (July 15, 1895), pp. 248, 249; *ibid.*, Vol. 2 (February 24, 1896), p. 251; *ibid.*, Vol. 2 (May 12, 1896), pp. 256-259.

[26] *Ibid.*, Vol. 2 (February 1, 1874), p. 207.

[27] *Minutes of the Board of Trustees*, Vol. 5 (March 11, 1896), p. 138.

[28] *Dean's Book*, Vol. 2 (April 1, 1897), pp. 269, 270.

Notes, Chapter 12

[1] *In Memory of Emil Alexander deSchweinitz*, Memorial Meeting Under Auspices of Columbian University, March 5, 1904 (Washington, 1904), pp. 3-9.

[2] *Dean's Book*, Vol. 2 (November 23, 1897), pp. 288-297; *ibid.*, Vol. 2 (December 18, 1897), p. 299.

[3] *Minutes of the Board of Trustees*, Vol. 5 (April 13, 1898), pp. 266-269; *ibid.*, Vol. 5 (June 1, 1898), p. 284; *ibid.*, Vol. 5 (January 11, 1899), p. 341.

[4] *Ibid.*, Vol. 5 (June 1, 1898), pp. 283, 284.

[5] *First Annual Report of the Board of Governors of the University Hospital* (Columbian) of Washington, D.C., 1335 H Street, N.W., November 1, 1898, to October 31, 1899, pp. 7, 8, 15, 16.

[6] *Dean's Book*, Vol. 2 (July 16, 1898, to December 12, 1898), pp. 311-324.

[7] *Minutes of the Board of Trustees*, Vol. 5 (June 1, 1898), pp. 280-283.

[8] *Records of the Proceedings of the Dental Department of the Columbian University, A.D. 1887*, Vol. 1 (December 27, 1887), pp. 3, 4.

9 *Ibid.*, Vol. 1 (March 16, 1888), p. 5; *ibid.*, Vol. 1 (September 24, 1888), p. 7; *ibid.*, Vol. 1 (March 26, 1889), p. 9; *ibid.*, Vol. 1 (March 21, 1890), p. 11.

10 *Ibid.*, Vol. 1 (September 28, 1891), p. 18.

11 *Ibid.*, Vol. 1 (May 6, 1894), p. 33; *ibid.*, Vol. 1 (June 2, 1894), p. 34.

12 *Ibid.*, Vol. 1 (January 31, 1895), pp. 37, 38; *ibid.*, Vol. 1 (May 14, 1898), p. 57.

13 *Ibid.*, Vol. 1 (May 21, 1901), p. 67.

14 *Dean's Book*, Vol. 2 (September 27, 1899), p. 338; *ibid.*, Vol. 2 (November 24, 1900), p. 359; *ibid.*, Vol. 2 (November 24, 1900), p. 360; *Minutes of the Board of Trustees*, Vol. 5 (November 29, 1897), p. 244; *ibid.*, Vol. 5 (January 11, 1899), p. 341; *ibid.*, Vol. 5 (January 9, 1901), p. 478; *ibid.*, Vol. 5 (March 8, 1902), p. 535.

15 *Dean's Book*, Vol. 2 (June 28, 1901), p. 368; *ibid.*, Vol. 2 (September 28, 1901), p. 370; *ibid.*, Vol. 2 (October 17-21, 1901) pp. 373-374; *ibid.*, Vol. 2 (November 2, 1901), pp. 375, 376; House of Representatives, 61st Cong., 3rd Sess., Doc. 1060, p. 86.

16 *Dean's Book*, Vol. 2 (June 23, 1902), p. 381; *ibid.*, Vol. 2 (September 27, 1902), p. 387; *ibid.*, Vol. 2 (October 10, 1902), p. 389.

17 *Ibid.*, Vol. 2 (January 6, 1903), p. 383; *ibid.*, Vol. 2 (January 10, 1903), p. 394; *ibid.*, Vol. 2 (February 21, 1903), p. 395; *ibid.*, Vol. 2 (February 28, 1903), p. 396; *ibid.*, Vol. 2 (March 14, 1903), pp. 398, 399.

18 *Ibid.*, Vol. 2 (July 12, 1902), p. 382.

19 These discussions continued throughout the meetings of the faculty from December 9, 1899, through June 28, 1901. *Dean's Book*, Vol. 2 (December 9, 1899, to June 28, 1901), pp. 341-368.

20 *Minutes of the Board of Trustees*, Vol. 6 (February 20, 1904), p. 168.

BIBLIOGRAPHICAL COMMENT ON CHAPTERS 13 TO 17

From 1910 on, we have to depend largely on the *Minutes of the Board of Trustees* which, for this period, are fortunately very full. Amplifying this material are the annual catalogues and a great mass of ephemeral material: student and alumni publications, committee reports, and campaign literature. Some of this material, such as *The Golden Book*, has been prepared with care and is of real value.

Notes, Chapter 13

1 *University Bulletin, The Columbian University, Washington, D.C.*, Announcements 1903-1904 (Washington, 1903), pp. 132-134.

2 Elmer Louis Kayser, *Bricks Without Straw, The Evolution of George Washington University* (New York, 1970), p. 231.

3 *Minutes of the Board of Trustees*, Vol. 5 (November 29, 1897), p. 244.

4 *University Bulletin*, p. 132.

5 *Dean's Book*, Vol. 2 (June 29, 1903), p. 403; *ibid.*, Vol. 2 (September 29, 1903), p. 405.

6 H. H. Donnally, "The Relation of Members of the Faculty of the George Washington University to Yellow Fever Investigations," *The George Washington University Bulletin*, Vol. 5, No. 3 (October, 1906), pp. 51-63.

7 Columbian University, *Ordinance Providing for the Organization and Conduct*

of the Department of Public Health, with courses of study, etc., adopted February 20, 1904, p. 5; *Columbian University Bulletin, March, 1904, Catalogue Number*, Vol. 3, No. 1 (Washington, 1904), p. 142.

[8] *In Memory of Emil Alexander deSchweinitz*, Memorial Meeting Under Auspices of Columbian University, March 5, 1904 (Washington, 1904), pp. 3, 22-29.

Notes, Chapter 14

[1] *Minutes of the Board of Trustees*, Vol. 6 (January 12, 1910), p. 533.

[2] *Dean's Book*, Vol. 2 (May 9, 1902).

[3] *Minutes of the Board of Trustees*, Vol. 6 (November 16, 1904), pp. 204 ff.

[4] *Ibid.*, Vol. 6 (January 8, 1908), p. 361; *ibid.*, Vol. 6 (May 7, 1908), p. 385; *ibid.*, Vol. 6 (April 5-10, 1908), pp. 454-456.

[5] *Ibid.*, Vol. 6 (April 23, 1909), p. 462.

[6] "A Notable Year," reprint from the *1965-66 Annual Report of the Carnegie Foundation for the Advancement of Teaching*, pp. 3-4.

[7] Abraham Flexner, *Medical Education in the United States and Canada*, with an Introduction by Henry S. Pritchett, The Carnegie Foundation for the Advancement of Teaching, Bulletin Number 4, 1910, pp. 154, 201-203. Questionable practices are referred to on pp. 22, 31, 32, 39, 112.

[8] For a detailed treatment of this period of reverses, see Elmer Louis Kayser, *Bricks Without Straw, The Evolution of George Washington University* (New York, 1970), pp. 173-212.

[9] Stat. at Large, 58th Cong., 3rd Sess., en. 1467, Vol. 33, Part 1, pp. 1036, 1037.

[10] *Minutes of the Board of Trustees*, Vol. 6 (January 11, 1905), pp. 232 ff.; *ibid.*, Vol. 6 (November 22, 1905), p. 268; Charles H. Stockton, "Historical Sketch of George Washington University, Washington, D.C.," *Records of the Columbia Historical Society*, Vol. 19, p. 125.

[11] *Ibid.*, p. 126; *Minutes of the Board of Trustees*, Vol. 5 (March 11, 1896), p. 138; *ibid.*, Vol. 5 (June 1, 1898), p. 284; *ibid.*, Vol. 6 (March 17, 1908), p. 369.

[12] *Ibid.*, Vol. 7 (June 4, 1913), p. 235; *ibid.*, Vol. 7 (October 27, 1913), p. 260; *Sixth Annual Report of the University Hospital*, 1904, pp. 27, 28.

[13] *Ibid.*, pp. 29-30.

[14] *The George Washington University Bulletin*, Vol. 7, No. 4 (December, 1908), pp. 103, 113.

[15] *Ibid.*, Vol. 3, No. 1 (March, 1904), p. 144.

Notes, Chapter 15

[1] Daniel L. Borden, "William Cline Borden, 1858-1934," *Medical Annals of the District of Columbia*, Vol. 5 (September, October, 1936), pp. 11-15.

[2] *Minutes of the Board of Trustees*, Vol. 7 (January 4, 1911), p. 104; *ibid.*, Vol. 7 (May 9, 1911), p. 108.

[3] *Ibid.*, Vol. 7 (April 3, 1917), p. 429.

[4] *Ibid.*, Vol. 7 (October 9, 1918), p. 511; *ibid.*, Vol. 7 (February 15, 1919), p. 529.

[5] Miss Mary Glasscock to Dr. D. L. Borden, September 23, 1918. Letter in University Collection.

[6] *Minutes of the Board of Trustees*, Vol. 6 (November 16, 1904), pp. 204 ff.; *ibid.*,

Vol. 7 (April 30, 1918), p. 483; *The George Washington University Bulletin,* Vol. 15, No. 4 (December, 1916), pp. 8 ff.

⁷ *Minutes of the Board of Trustees,* Vol. 7 (October 9, 1918), p. 513; *The George Washington University Bulletin,* Catalogue Number, Vol. 17, No. 1 (March, 1918), p. 162.

⁸ *Minutes of the Board of Trustees,* Vol. 8 (February 18, 1920), p. 10.

⁹ *Ibid.,* Vol. 7 (June 11, 1919), pp. 553, 556; *ibid.,* Vol. 8 (March 19, 1920), p. 11; *ibid.,* Vol. 8 (April 3, 1920), pp. 18-20; Borden, *op. cit.,* pp. 13-15.

¹⁰ *Minutes of the Board of Trustees,* Vol. 8 (April 27, 1926), p. 382; *ibid.,* Vol. 8 (January 19, 1927), pp. 391 ff.; *ibid.,* Vol. 8 (May 18, 1927), p. 415; *ibid.,* Vol. 9 (January 12, 1937), p. 253.

¹¹ *Ibid.,* Vol. 8 (December 26, 1929), p. 529.

Notes, Chapter 16

¹ *Minutes of the Board of Trustees,* Vol. 9 (October 8, 1931), p. 17; *ibid.,* Vol. 9 (July, 1939), p. 409; *ibid.,* Vol. 9 (March 10, 1932), p. 38.

² *Ibid.,* Vol. 9 (December 10, 1931), p. 25; *ibid.,* Vol. 9 (June 28, 1934), p. 141; *ibid.,* Vol. 9 (May 31, 1935), p. 195; *ibid.,* Vol. 9 (July 6, 1936), p. 243.

³ *GW Medicine* (Fall, 1967), p. 4.

⁴ *Ibid.,* Memorial Issue (September, 1972), pp. 1-15.

⁵ Sir William Osler, *Aequanimitas* (New York, 1963), p. 90.

⁶ George Washington University, School of Medicine, *Catalogue of Intensive Postgraduate Courses,* 1955, p. 5.

⁷ *Minutes of the Board of Trustees,* Vol. 10 (December 12, 1940), p. 7; *ibid.,* Vol. 10 (November 12, 1941), p. 69; *ibid.,* Vol. 10 (December 10, 1942), p. 117; *ibid.,* Vol. 10 (October 20, 1943), p. 151.

Notes, Chapter 17

¹ *Minutes of the Board of Trustees,* Vol. 10 (December 14, 1944), pp. 207-209; *ibid.,* Vol. 10 (December 15, 1945), p. 262; *ibid.,* Vol. 10 (July 30, 1946), pp. 304, 305.

² *Ibid.,* Vol. 10 (December 12, 1946), p. 326; *ibid.,* Vol. 10 (October 9, 1947), p. 372; *ibid.,* Vol. 10 (July 21, 1948), p. 428.

³ *Ibid.,* Vol. 10 (December 14, 1944), pp. 195, 196; *ibid.,* Vol. 10 (February 10, 1949), pp. 471-474.

⁴ *The George Washington University Hospital,* Pennsylvania Avenue at Washington Circle (Washington, 1948), pp. 3, 5; *The Golden Book of The George Washington University Hospital* (Washington, 1949), pp. 5, 6.

⁵ *Minutes of the Board of Trustees,* Vol. 11 (January 13, 1956), pp. 458, 459; *ibid.,* Vol. 11 (February 9, 1956), pp. 481, 482; *ibid.,* Vol. 12 (June 20, 1956), pp. 21, 22; *ibid.,* Vol. 12 (October 13, 1960), p. 360; *ibid.,* Vol. 12 (December 14, 1961), p. 460.

⁶ *Ibid.,* Vol. 12 (February 8, 1962), p. 484.

⁷ *G.W. Medical News,* The George Washington University Medical Center (January 10, 1966), pp. 1, 2.

⁸ News release, March 20, 1969, The George Washington University, Medical Public Relations.

⁹ *New Look at G.W.U.,* release of Medical Public Relations, 1972.

PRESIDENTS OF THE UNIVERSITY

1821–1827	WILLIAM STAUGHTON
1828–1841	STEPHEN CHAPIN
1843–1854	JOEL SMITH BACON
1855–1858	JOSEPH GETCHELL BINNEY
1859–1871	GEORGE WHITEFIELD SAMSON
1871–1894	JAMES CLARKE WELLING
1894–1895	SAMUEL HARRISON GREENE, ACTING
1895–1900	BENAIAH L. WHITMAN
1900–1902	SAMUEL HARRISON GREENE, ACTING
1902–1910	CHARLES WILLIS NEEDHAM
1910–1918	CHARLES HERBERT STOCKTON
1918–1921	WILLIAM MILLER COLLIER
1921–1923	HOWARD L. HODGKINS, *ad interim*
1923–1927	WILLIAM MATHER LEWIS
1927–1959	CLOYD HECK MARVIN
1959–1961	OSWALD SYMISTER COLCLOUGH, ACTING
1961–1964	THOMAS HENRY CARROLL
1964–1965	OSWALD SYMISTER COLCLOUGH, ACTING
1965–	LLOYD HARTMAN ELLIOTT

HEADS OF THE MEDICAL DEPARTMENT

During the first half of its history, the faculty had two officers: a president or chairman (the title varies) and a dean. The president was the senior member of the faculty and was regularly reelected year after year. The dean was elected for a term of one year by rotation from the faculty list in order of seniority. The president for the time was excused from holding the office of dean. Recalling that during this period, the Medical Department was proprietary in character, the president's or chairman's relation to the faculty was roughly analogous to that of the president of Columbian College to the faculty of the parent institution. The dean kept records, received fees from students, and handled such business matters as were not referred to special committees. As the proprietary status was modified and then abolished, the need for a president or chairman ceased to exist and the office was discontinued. At the same time, the annual deanship disappears and deans hold their office for indefinite terms. In 1972, the office of vice president for medical affairs was created.

In view of the difficulties that it presents, it is understandable that no previous effort had been made to compile such a list, nor are the records so organized that the information is always available. For long periods the reference is simply to "the dean," with no name given. Consequently there are gaps in the list below. The date that precedes the name is the year of election, held usually in April or May following the close of the lectures for the year. The newly elected dean assumed his duties immediately or as soon as his accounts were audited; he served for the following academic year.

DEANS

1825	Thomas Henderson, M.D.
1826	Thomas Henderson, M.D.
1827	Nicholas W. Worthington, M.D.
1828	Frederick May, M.D.
1829	James M. Staughton, M.D.
1830	Thomas P. Jones, M.D.
1831-1834	No record of election
1834-1839	Exercises suspended
1839	J. Frederick May, M.D.
1840	John M. Thomas, M.D.
1841	Thomas Miller, M.D.
1842	Harvey Lindsly, M.D.
1843	W. P. Johnston, M.D.
1844	W. P. Johnston, M.D.
1845	W. P. Johnston, M.D.
1846	W. P. Johnston, M.D.
1849	W. P. Johnston, M.D.
1850	Joshua Riley, M.D.
1851	J. Frederick May, M.D.

1852	Grafton Tyler, M.D.
1853	Robert King Stone, M.D.
1854	Lewis H. Steiner, M.D.
1855	Thomas Miller, M.D.
1856	W. P. Johnston, M.D.
1857	James J. Waring, M.D.
1858	Joshua Riley, M.D.
1859 (June)	James J. Waring, M.D.
1859 (August)	John C. Riley, M.D. (Served until his death in 1879, though formal elections were held only in the years shown.)
1860	John C. Riley, M.D.
1863-1865	Exercises suspended
1869	John C. Riley, M.D.
1870	John C. Riley, M.D.
1879	A. F. A. King, M.D.
1894	D. Kerfoot Shute, M.D.
1897	Emil Alexander deSchweinitz, M.D.
1904	William F. R. Phillips, M.D.
1909	William Cline Borden, M.D.
1931	Earl Baldwin McKinley, M.D. (Served until his death in 1938)
1938	Walter A. Bloedorn, M.D.
1957	John L. Parks, M.D.
1972	James J. Feffer, M.D. (Acting)

PRESIDENTS OR CHAIRMEN OF THE FACULTY

Thomas Sewall, M.D., served as Chairman of the Faculty from its organization until his death in 1844.

1845	Thomas Miller, M.D. (Served until 1855)
1855	W. P. Johnston, M.D.
1856	Joshua Riley, M.D.
1857	W. P. Johnston, M.D.
1860	Thomas Miller, M.D.
1874	W. P. Johnston, M.D. (Apparently served until his death in 1876 and was succeeded by Alexander Y. P. Garnett [d. July 11, 1888])
1887	J. Ford Thompson, M.D.

The designation "president of the faculty" was dropped by action of the faculty March 5, 1898.

VICE PRESIDENTS FOR MEDICAL AFFAIRS

1972   John L. Parks, M.D.
            (Served until his death, July 5, 1972)
1972   James J. Feffer, M.D.

INDEX